C000252700

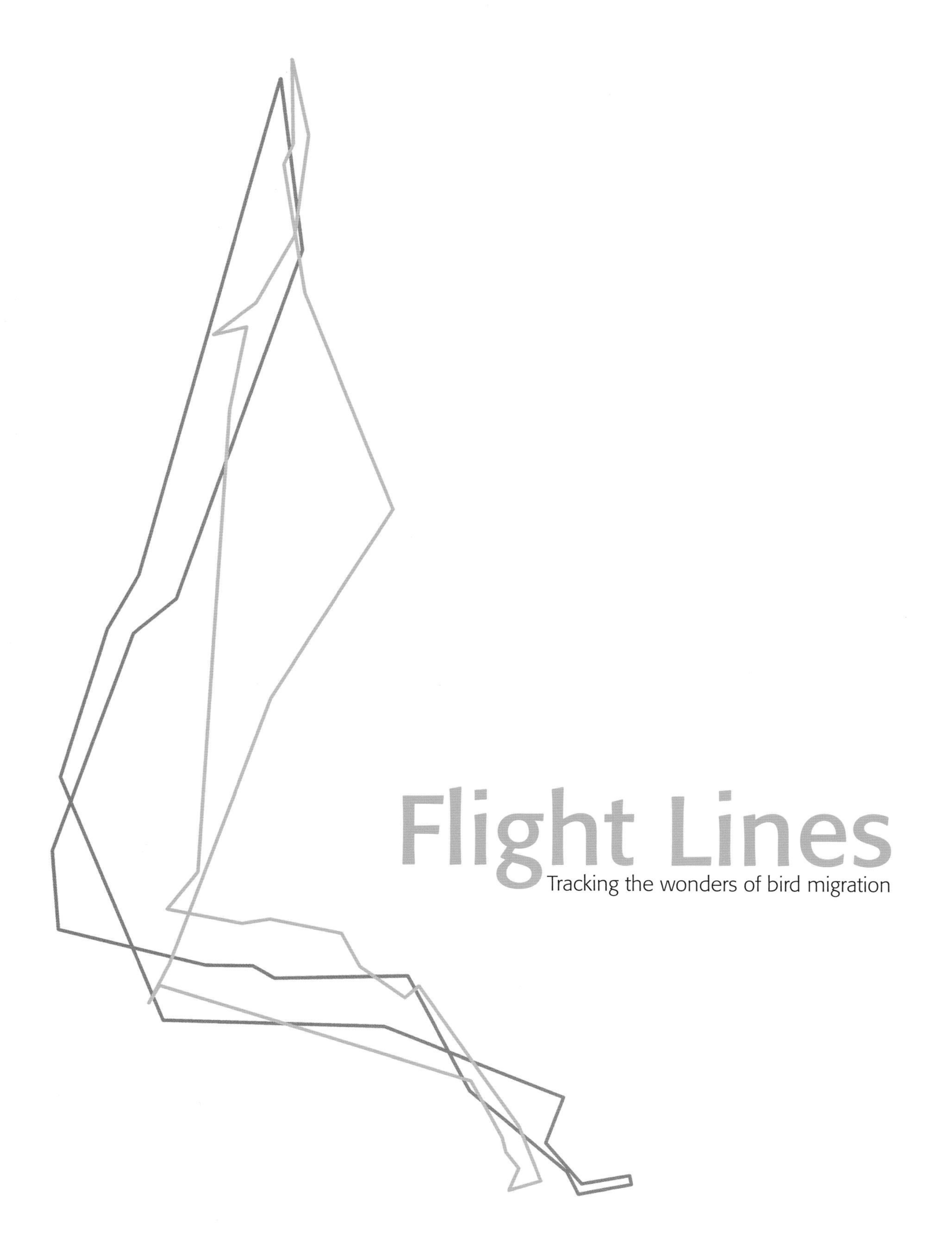

Flight Lines

Tracking the wonders of bird migration

First published in the United Kingdom in 2017 by the British Trust for Ornithology,
The Nunnery, Thetford, Norfolk, IP24 2PU. www.bto.org

Design and Layout by Mike Toms & Esther Tyson

ISBN 978-1-908581-77-8

Printed and bound in Italy by Printer Trento, an FSC® certified company for printing books on FSC mixed papers in compliance with the chain of custody and on-product labelling standards. Printer Trento has an ISO 14001 certified environmental management system.

Flight Lines

Tracking the wonders of bird migration

Written by Mike Toms

Where art and science meet

Whether it is the sight of the season's first Swallow or the sound of a spring Cuckoo, the return of our summer migrants delivers a reassuring sense of a globe that, as the poet Ted Hughes once described, *'is still working'*. That birds should undertake such long and dangerous migratory journeys is something that has long fascinated us, prompting works of art and literature, not to mention many thousands of scientific studies.

Now, at a time when many of our migrant birds are in decline, this fascination with migration has even more relevance. Our combined interest can be used to fund and support much-needed research, such as the work being done by the BTO and its partners, and to secure wider engagement with these iconic birds. The BTO's Flight Lines project, a joint initiative with the Society of Wildlife Artists (SWLA), seeks to highlight the challenges that migrant birds face and brings to a wider audience the research and conservation work that is being done to help them.

By partnering SWLA artists with BTO researchers and volunteers we have been able to document our summer migrants – and those who study them – in a new and engaging way. While science can provide the evidence, making the case for conservation action and monitoring progress towards its goals, the creative arts deliver passion and engagement. Together, science and art make a stronger case for the conservation of migrant birds, engaging new voices in support of conservation action.

This book follows the journeys of the birds that migrate between Britain and Africa, from their departure in autumn to their return in spring. The chapters follow this seasonal cycle and take you on the journeys made by migrant birds. As will become clear from the text, the birds touch many different peoples and cultures along the way. We hope that you will enjoy this book and the narrative it gives to the artwork and research emerging from the BTO/SWLA Flight Lines project.

Kim Atkinson
Assessing fat levels on a Goldcrest
Oil pastel and pen

The journey

Autumn departures

The journey starts here. It is not yet dawn, but the clear autumn sky and soft glow emanating from nearby Hastings provide sufficient light for us to work by. The chill in the air makes me grateful that we are moving about, walking the paths and unfurling the nets that will soon hold our first catch of the day. It is a familiar enough scene to anyone involved in bird ringing, but there is one difference here and that is the soundscape. From all over the site come the songs of migrant warblers, pipits and other species – a rich dawn chorus that makes a lie of the September date displayed on my mobile phone. This chorus of sound does not come from the birds – although I suspect that many of these species are here – but emanates instead from loudspeakers, hidden around the site and positioned to attract nocturnal migrants to this small patch of East Sussex countryside, adjoining the Pett Level.

As the ringing totals from this site reveal, the deceit is a successful one. On a typical autumn day many hundreds of birds may be caught in the nets and processed, generating important information on the movement patterns and survival rates of those birds passing out of Britain via the south coast. As the autumn progresses, so a succession of different species pass through on migration, underlining that the departures do not happen all at once. The nature of the breeding season, the pattern of post-breeding moult and many other factors will influence the timing by which these summer visitors depart our shores to begin their journey south.

The arrival of dawn and the first round of checking the nets reveals many of the migrant birds that have stopped here to refuel, before crossing the English Channel. Sedge Warblers and Blackcaps are the dominant species in the nets today, but a handful of Grasshopper Warblers and a single Aquatic Warbler reinforce the sense that we are very fortunate to be able to experience these amazing creatures at such close quarters. It is, however, the sheer numbers of individuals passing through this one site that really brings home to me the scale of this annual movement of birds to and from their breeding grounds. It has been estimated – using some sound assumptions and careful calculations – that in excess of two billion birds migrate from Europe to their African wintering grounds each year, crossing both the Mediterranean and the Sahara in the process. This staggering figure represents roughly one in four of all of the birds breeding in Europe. Viewed at a global scale, and as noted by Reginald Moreau in his seminal paper on the migration system that links Europe to Africa, bird migration represents '*a seasonal ecological adjustment on a gigantic scale*'. Those birds leaving western Europe are part of a wider flyway, known to ornithologists as the Palearctic–Afrotropical Migration System, which sees birds from breeding grounds across Europe and Asia head to the vast African continent. We are predominantly interested in the birds from the western end of this system, those that leave Britain in autumn, move through continental Europe and winter in Africa, largely south of the Sahara; we tend to refer to these birds as Afro-Palearctic migrants.

The departure of these summer visitors marks the start of another cycle; those birds that journeyed north in spring are now joined by a new generation, making the flight south for the first time. Perhaps the fact that these birds bred here gives us some false perception of ownership and it is little wonder that we think of them as ours. That they should feature so prominently in our literature, art and culture reflects the strong affinity that we have with them. But it is important to remember that most of these birds spend the greater part of the year away from our shores, often many thousands of miles away from us in Africa. Male Cuckoos, for example, spend just a few weeks on their UK breeding grounds, arriving in late April or early May and departing as early as the first week of June.

We are not the only people who spend time with these long distance travellers, so it is right that we should understand the influence they have on the lives of others, living elsewhere. It is not just the wintering grounds that we should consider but also the landscapes and peoples present along the migration routes taken by these birds. Over the course of a few days or weeks, a migrating bird may pass through many different countries; perhaps it will be seen by many different human eyes and prompt some recognition as a seasonal visitor, marking the time of year.

These individual birds connect us with other lands and other communities, something made all the more poignant by the knowledge that migrant birds, on their autumn crossing of the Mediterranean, may overfly migrants of a different sort – refugees making the dangerous journey north in search of hope and opportunity. What happens to these birds, both to individuals and their populations, will depend on how all of us come together to understand the threats they face and what we need to do to ensure that the spectacle of migration continues.

Why migrate?

But why should so many birds risk such a long and dangerous journey, a journey which they will repeat twice a year throughout their short lives? Different hypotheses have been put forward to explain why almost 20% of the world's 10,000 bird species undertake long and perilous journeys on an annual basis. The one of these with a good deal of evidence in support of it, is that birds migrate in order to benefit from the seasonal availability of resources, such as the burst of invertebrate life seen in the northern hemisphere summer. Interestingly, it is not necessarily the total amount of resources available that is important but the surplus that remains once the needs of resident, non-migratory, species have been met. This underlines the competition that may be inherent within these breeding communities, made up of both migrants and residents.

For the Afro-Palearctic migrants, which evolved in Africa, the evidence suggests that there has been an elongation of their migratory flights over time, the birds eventually reaching Europe as conditions continued to change. One important consideration is the risk of making these journeys in the first place. Predation, bad weather and other hazards may lead to increased mortality, and longer journeys may mean greater risk – though not always. Overall, it is this balance between risk and benefit that may help to shape bird communities at a global scale.

The nature of bird communities is something that has long interested those researchers working in the field of macro-ecology. One such researcher is Marius Somveille, now based at the Edward Grey Institute of Field Ornithology in Oxford. Through a PhD at the University of Cambridge, and working with colleagues from both Cambridge and Montpelier, Somveille has examined the different hypotheses, seeking to explain the documented global patterns in migratory bird diversity. The results of Somveille's work, which builds on work done in the 1970s by Carlos Herrera, show that seasonality is a key driver of the number of migrants present within breeding bird communities. Arriving migrants, such as those species reaching Britain in April and May, benefit from the surplus in resources available to them during our northern summer. Harsh winter weather limits the populations of resident birds, keeping them at a level well below that which could be sustained by the resources available during the breeding season months; this provides an opportunity for other species to move into Britain during spring to take advantage of the resulting surplus.

Of course this is only part of the story, since what happens during migration and on the wintering grounds will also have a role to play. Somveille's work suggests that the resources available to migrants on their wintering areas, coupled with the location of these relative to the breeding grounds, are important. Migrants leaving their breeding grounds are likely to stop preferentially at the nearest suitable wintering sites, leading, for example, to a concentration of non-breeding birds in the southern latitudes of the northern hemisphere. For the migrant birds that breed in Britain, this means a concentration of wintering migrants in southern Europe and Central and West Africa, south of the Sahara. What happens to them here, and while on migration, will influence the numbers that return to our shores the following spring.

Changing times

Migration is not a static process; instead it is something that changes over time and also shows variation between, or even within, individual species and their populations. It seems difficult to imagine that, for example, the Lesser Black-backed Gull was almost entirely migratory in habits prior to the 1950s, with only occasional birds remaining in Britain year-round. More recently, we have seen a rapid increase in the numbers of Chiffchaffs and Blackcaps wintering here, though for different reasons, and falling numbers of wintering Whooper Swans, birds that are now 'short-stopping' on migration and wintering further north. Indeed, over a wide range of latitudes it appears that many bird populations have become increasingly sedentary, losing the migratory habit or shifting towards becoming a partial migrant – where only part of the population migrates in any given year. The driving force behind many of these changes is climate change, the effects of which are likely to see some bird species wintering further north than previously, arriving earlier on their breeding grounds and leaving later; these are things that are increasingly evident from BTO data sets.

In order to understand such effects, we first need to tackle the questions of how migration arose and what helps to maintain it today. Much of Europe was covered with ice during the last ice age, meaning that many of the movements made by birds now migrating to and from Britain would have evolved within the last 10,000–14,000 years. This seems a relatively short amount of time in an evolutionary context, but it is important to realise that the features and behaviours which support a migratory lifestyle have not evolved from nothing; they were already present in non-migratory populations of birds and short-distance migrants.

At it simplest, a potential migrant needs seasonal fat reserves to fuel the journey, a mechanism for making the decision to migrate at the right time, and the ability to navigate the route. There are measurable differences between migrants and non-migrants, even within a species. Migrants usually have longer and more pointed wings, shorter tails and smaller bodies than non-migrants. These features are more efficient for longer level flight, whereas short wings and long tails provide greater manoeuvrability and aid escape from predators. Migratory populations of Blackcaps have a different

Dafila Scott
Whitethroat family II
Pastel

wing shape to sedentary populations, underlining that they are trading off the flight efficiency that comes from longer wings against decreased manoeuvrability and increased predation risk. The aspect ratio of a wing – which describes a wing's shape and is calculated by taking the wing span squared and dividing it by wing area – is also strongly correlated with migration distance.

Migratory bird species also have a more highly developed hippocampus, the part of the avian brain that delivers spatial memory, and a larger optic lobe, features that support finding your way while migrating. Interestingly, while the relative size of the optic lobe has been found to be strongly correlated with migration distance in a large number of migratory birds, overall relative brain mass decreases with increasing migration distance. A large brain is heavier than a small one and is energetically that much more expensive to operate. There is, however, one aspect that is more difficult to understand and that is the evolution of a directional preference, sufficient to see a bird to and from a wintering area that may lay many thousands of miles from where it was born. Since the young of most species undertake their first migratory journey unaccompanied by their parents, getting to and from the wintering grounds and potentially stopping along the way to refuel is not something that is learned; instead it has to be innate.

Should I stay or should I go?

In many respects it is misleading to split species into being either migratory or sedentary in their habits, since both types of behaviour may be found within a single population of a particular species. In fact, individual birds may switch between being migratory or being sedentary, the decision often based on the availability of key resources and leading to what is known as 'partial migration'. The Goldfinch is a good example of such a species, with British birds showing a range of movement patterns. Many Goldfinches winter close to their breeding sites, while others move south at the end of the breeding season and cross into France, before moving down into Spain where they overwinter. Others leave Britain and head south-east, reaching Belgium and the Low Countries. Individuals that have moved south do not appear to be heading to a particular wintering area, but instead seem to stop once they find suitable conditions. At least a few Goldfinches cross into North Africa, but the sparse nature of the ring-recovery data set (which holds encounters with ringed birds) for North African countries means that we do not have any real idea of the actual numbers involved. Ring-recovery data do, however, reveal that individual Goldfinches may do different things in different years, perhaps wintering in Britain one winter and then in Spain in a subsequent year. For migration to be a successful strategy it needs to enable individuals to survive and breed better than would have been the case were they to have remained in the breeding area throughout the year. That natural selection can shape the evolution of migration strategies can be seen by the case of the Blackcap, a familiar species to birdwatchers here in the UK, including those who feed their garden birds throughout the year.

Sixty years ago the Blackcap was a common summer visitor, rarely observed outside of the breeding season, but since the 1960s we have seen an increasing number of individuals using garden feeding stations during the winter months. A growing body of research has revealed that Blackcaps breeding in southern Germany and Austria have tended increasingly to migrate in a north-westerly direction during the autumn, bringing them to Britain, rather than taking the traditional south-westerly route that would have led them to wintering areas located in southern Spain and North Africa. This new strategy is genetically encoded and maintained because the birds adopting the migration route have become reproductively isolated from those following the traditional route. Not only this, but the Blackcaps wintering in Britain secure the best territories when they return to their breeding areas come spring, arriving earlier than birds that have wintered further south and, as a result, producing more young.

The question of why Britain has become such a successful wintering destination for German and Austrian Blackcaps has been addressed by Kate Plummer and colleagues at the BTO, who used BTO Garden BirdWatch data to look at the role of temperature and the provision of supplementary foods at garden feeding stations. The results of this work reveal that Blackcaps are becoming increasingly associated with the provision of supplementary food, and that the reliability of this food provisioning is shaping their wintering distribution at a national scale. Local climatic conditions, notably local temperature, also play a significant role, suggesting that the increased availability of food, coupled with a warming climate and more favourable winter weather conditions, has supported the establishment of this migration route.

Migrants in decline

The Blackcap study shows the influence that human activities can have on migrant birds and their populations. Such influence can be far-reaching, resulting in population declines or even the local extinction of particular populations. There is growing evidence that many of the small birds that migrate between western Europe and Africa are in decline, with these declines often more pronounced than those seen in resident species, or short-distance migrants. Long-distance migrants, such as those breeding in Britain and wintering south of the Sahara, are likely to be more susceptible to environmental change because of their complex annual cycle and dependence upon a series of different places, each of which is

of importance to the species at a particular time in the year. The two most important factors, contributing to the widespread decline in our summer migrants, are human-related habitat change and a changing climate, the latter also linked to human activities.

Some of these changes are taking place here in Britain, reducing the availability of suitable breeding habitat and the resources required to secure a new generation of individuals. Intensification of agriculture, changes in woodland management and increasing deer populations, for example, have played their part in the long-term population declines witnessed in Yellow Wagtail, Corncrake, Turtle Dove and Nightingale. In some cases changes to favoured breeding habitat can have a dramatic impact on breeding populations; wetland drainage in south-west Belarus since the 1960s has, for example, resulted in the loss of nearly 90% of the Aquatic Warbler's breeding habitat, leaving the species now listed as 'globally threatened'. This makes the individual caught in our nets in Sussex all the more special – it is one of just a handful that will be caught along England's south coast this year. That Aquatic Warblers use our south coast sites makes these places even more important for the conservation of migrating birds.

Changes elsewhere may also shape the populations of migrant birds breeding in Britain. We know, for example, that drought in West Africa brought about sudden and precipitous declines in Whitethroat, and that the abundance of Sand Martin and Sedge Warbler in Britain has varied in relation to West African rainfall patterns. However, land use change in Africa is perhaps the most important factor in the decline of migrants wintering within the Sahel region of West Africa; as we shall see later, attempts to reduce its impact face some significant political challenges.

Where our migrants spend the winter, and the habitats that they use there, may influence what is happening to their breeding populations here in Britain. We know that some of our migrants winter within the arid Sahelian zone of West Africa. Others use the Sahel as a stopover site, before moving further south, either to winter in the humid tropical zone or south of the equator. Some overfly the Sahel altogether, taking them straight to the humid tropical zone or to other regions within the vast African continent. These different regions vary in how much rainfall they receive and in the seasonal pattern of its occurrence. Rainfall volumes in West Africa are strongly determined by latitude, and these in turn determine vegetation growth and invertebrate abundance, the latter of particular importance to small migrant birds.

The relationships between where Afro-Palearctic migrants winter and what is happening to their populations here in Britain has been examined by BTO researchers, using data on breeding population trends from the BTO/JNCC/RSPB Breeding Bird Survey for the period from 1994 to 2008.

Jane Smith
Corncrake
Screen print

We know that many of the species using the arid zone – such as the Whitethroat, Sedge Warbler and Sand Martin just mentioned – suffered sharp declines prior to this period, but there are other species for which the declines fall within the period covered by the Breeding Bird Survey. The results of this work underline that the region within which Afro-Palearctic migrants winter, and the type of habitat used there, are important factors affecting the population trends seen here in the UK. Species that winter within the humid tropical zone of West and Central Africa, together with those that winter in southern Africa, declined more rapidly between 1994 and 2008 than migrant species wintering elsewhere. Alarmingly, all but one of the species that winter within the humid tropical zone show a negative population trend; the exception being House Martin, a species about which we know particularly little when it comes to the part of the year spent outside of the breeding areas. Being an aerial feeder, there is the opportunity for this species to respond more readily to spatial variation in food availability.

Although we lack detailed knowledge on the habitats used by many of the migrants wintering within Africa, the broad patterns are known to us. Using this information, the BTO team examining wintering behaviour and population trend also discovered that those species classified as wintering predominantly within open landscapes and woodland show significantly more negative population trends than those species using other habitats. As we will see later in the book, the changing nature of land use within Africa may have significant consequences for those migratory birds using the region. It is also worth noting that the migrant story isn't as simple as birds moving between a breeding area and a wintering area; in order to undertake these vast journeys small birds have to refuel at stopover sites, some of which are located within areas that are used by other birds for wintering.

Fattening up

Migration can be energetically expensive, particularly where individual birds have to make very long and continuous flights over inhospitable terrain. In general, birds that migrate over areas of favourable habitat tend to make a series of short flights, taking on board sufficient food to lay down the small amounts of body fat needed to fuel each leg of the journey. Birds that have to cross unfavourable habitat tend to lay down much larger fat reserves, sometimes almost doubling their body weight in the process; they may also make significant changes to their body structure.

Most of the energy used to fuel a migratory flight comes from the stores of fat laid down before the bird sets off. Fat is a highly efficient fuel, delivering up to nine times more energy than alternatives and, importantly, also releasing an equal weight of water during the process of its oxidation.

The downside of using fat, beyond the additional costs of having to carry the extra weight, is that its metabolism requires small amounts of protein to be broken down as part of the process – at least 5% of the energy released during a migratory flight comes from protein. The fat is laid down in various parts of the body, most notably under the skin, around the digestive organs and within the tracheal pit (located within the furcula, or 'wishbone'). Bird ringers routinely 'score' the amount of fat present on a bird by blowing gently on the chest, belly and flank feathers to reveal the skin beneath. Fat deposited in these areas shows as a pale yellow substance pressed against the skin. In birds that are about to undertake a long migratory flight, the whole body can appear waxy yellow, so substantial are the fat reserves laid down. As we have just noted, the amount of fat deposited is usually matched to the distance that the bird will have to cover during its flight. Carrying too much fat may make it harder for a bird to avoid a predator, while carrying too little may see the bird die of exhaustion.

Migratory flights are typically preceded by several days of intense feeding, as the bird attempts to secure the fat reserves needed. The amount of time involved will not only depend upon the size of the reserves required but also on the type of food being eaten and the ease with which it can be digested and turned into fat. During migration individual birds effectively have to switch from a 'fuelling mode' to a 'flight mode', often more than once. The two different modes favour different things; during the fuelling mode a large digestive system is advantageous, enabling the bird to process quantities of food far in excess of those normally handled. During the flight mode the digestive system becomes part of the baggage – additional weight that has to be carried – and it is instead large muscles, a strong circulatory system and a well-functioning heart that become important. Interestingly, some long distance migrants can make dramatic changes to their body structure when switching modes; breast muscles may be enlarged, as may the heart, while other organs – such as the digestive tract and the reproductive organs – may shrink, reducing their contribution to body mass.

England's south coast and the English Channel beyond provide a natural barrier to the southwards movements of departing migrants, and many birds pause here to refuel. In the case of the Sedge Warblers, so abundant in the nets set at Icklesham in East Sussex, a series of 'pre-migratory' movements sees them gather at those reedbed sites supporting high densities of the Mealy Plum Aphid. These aphids provide an ephemeral but abundant food resource, prompting many British and Irish Sedge Warblers to stop at reedbed sites in South Wales, southern England and northern France. Mealy Plum Aphid numbers are at their seasonal peak here but populations further south, in southern France for example, will have long passed their peak

Richard Johnson
Bluethroat, Fair Isle
Watercolour

Richard Johnson
Whinchat, Blakeney
Watercolour

Darren Woodhead
In the hand studies
Watercolour

25th September 2015.

Nik Pollard
Whitethroat studies
Mixed media

by the time that the warblers arrive. This may be why most of our Sedge Warblers fuel so far north, preparing them for rapid long haul flights that will take them towards their wintering grounds south of the Sahara, without significant additional fattening along the way. This pattern of pre-migratory fattening differs from that adopted by the Sedge Warbler's relative, the Reed Warbler, which instead makes a series of shorter flights south, pausing to refuel in France and Portugal, before stopping again in North Africa to take on sufficient fat reserves to make the desert crossing.

The ephemeral nature of the aphid populations tends to concentrate the autumn passage of Sedge Warblers through key sites within a short time window. In contrast, our Reed Warblers do not appear to be quite so limited in the times and places where they can build up their fat reserves, so they tend to be present at stopover sites over a longer period of time. The two species also show some differences in their feeding techniques. Sedge Warblers feed mainly by picking at prey that is resting on the surface of the vegetation and concentrate on the aphids. Reed Warblers use this technique too but they more often fly-catch to take insects on the wing, additionally exploiting a much broader suite of other invertebrate species. That two closely-related species should adopt very different strategies to their autumn migration underlines that migrating birds have a number of different options available to them when it comes to making the journey south.

Michael Schaub and Lucas Jenni drew on ringing data, collected from sites right across Europe and into North Africa, to tease out some of the other approaches to fuelling the autumn migration. Their examination of hundreds of birds, from six small migrant species, revealed four different approaches to fuelling the journey south. As just noted for Sedge Warbler, some species accumulate very large reserves of fat well before they reach the Sahara – the main barrier facing our migrant birds on their autumn migration – and use these reserves to fuel a single, very long flight straight to the wintering grounds. Pied Flycatcher is another of our summer migrants that appears to adopt this strategy. Other species, such as Garden Warbler, make a series of shorter flights, refuelling at each 'stopover' but taking on more fuel than is needed for the next leg of the journey. Birds adopting this strategy gradually accumulate more fat reserves as they move further south, preparing them for the desert crossing ahead. Reed Warblers and Whitethroats also make short flights, but only take on enough fuel for the next leg of their journey; their final stop, just before the desert, sees them lay down the far bigger fat reserves needed for the flight across the desert. A final group of species, which include some shrikes and Spotted Flycatcher, follow a similar strategy to Reed Warbler and Whitethroat but don't take on large reserves ahead of the desert crossing; instead it appears that they rely on finding food at oases as they cross.

Moult and migration

Old or damaged feathers need to be replaced in order to assist the regulation of body temperature and the maintenance of high levels of flight performance. They may also be replaced in order to change the appearance of an individual, for example when moulting from non-breeding to breeding plumage, or to aid reproduction, such as the development of a brood patch. Moult is energetically expensive and may also affect an individual's ability to fly and avoid predators. Because of this, its timing has to fit in with other important components of the annual cycle, most notably reproduction and migration. Most of the small birds found breeding in Europe usually renew their entire plumage at least once a year, typically within a short and well-defined period. Larger birds moult their feathers over a longer period, perhaps replacing just a few flight feathers in a given year. This difference reflects different energetic costs and the impact that a more complete moult would have on the flight performance of a larger bird.

Most our of birds undergo moult at the end of the breeding season, a period during which individuals tend not to have other commitments. Long-distance migrants, however, may be under pressure to begin the journey south. Some may begin their moult here in Europe by moulting some of their body or contour feathers but leaving the flight feathers untouched; others will not initiate any moult until they reach their wintering grounds in Africa. It is in Africa that many long-distance migrants moult flight feathers, though even here there appears to be some variation in timing, both between and within species. Some Reed Warblers, for example, replace all of their flight feathers over a short period; others, notably those moving further south and east within the winter, may suspend their wing moult part way through, picking it up again once they have reached a new wintering destination. While the separation of moult and migration into distinct periods within the annual cycle is usually fairly rigid, for some species it has to be more flexible. This is certainly the case for Swallows, Sand Martins and House Martins, which occasionally replace some of their flight feathers while still in Europe – most, however, are replaced within Africa.

Young birds, which have grown juvenile plumage while in the nest, may follow a different pattern to that seen in the adults. Juvenile body plumage tends to be rather sparse, the youngster putting its limited resources into other components – such as the skeleton, muscles and flight feathers – rather than those that merely provide insulation. This plumage is replaced during the post-juvenile moult which, in most small long-distance migrants, begins soon after the bird has left the nest, progressing rapidly ahead of the individual's first migration. In some species, such as Redstart, migratory restlessness and the deposition of fat reserves for the journey ahead, typically begin even before the post-juvenile moult has been completed,

Carry Akroyd
Swifts and drain
Serigraph

such is the pressure to be on the move. Juvenile Lesser Whitethroats, for example, may begin their journey south when they are just a month old and still actively moulting the contour feathers on their wings.

It is not just moult that may influence the timing of departure or be curtailed by the pressure to begin migration. It is well known that, from late July or early August onwards, Turtle Doves begin to gather together in flocks ahead of departure. Such is the time pressure to join these flocks that some individuals abandon recently started breeding attempts that may involve eggs or even young chicks. There is evidence that the Turtle Dove breeding season is now shorter – by some 12 days – than it was during the 1960s; much of this difference has been linked to earlier autumn departures, raising the question of the impact of this change on the reproductive output of these rapidly declining birds.

Reedbed nights

Our knowledge of the migration strategies of birds like Reed Warbler, Whitethroat and Swallow comes from several sources, including information collected by ringers, laboratory experiments conducted by academics and from the new generation of tracking devices that enable us to follow migrating birds. While laboratory experiments and tracking devices tend to provide a great deal of detail about a small number of individuals, often from discrete sites or populations, bird ringing allows us to look across populations and to place the more detailed findings into a wider context. As we have just seen from the work of Michael Schaub and Lucas Jenni, the coordinated collection of ringing data at large spatial scales can tell us a great deal. This approach has been particularly useful in examining the extent to which Swallows store fat prior to their autumn migration.

Since Swallows feed on small insects, caught on the wing, it was assumed that migrating Swallows could feed as they went, removing the need to build up large fat reserves prior to departure. However the EURING Swallow Project, which ran from 1997 until 2002, set out to test this by using a network of bird ringers to catch the birds as they gathered to roost ahead of their autumn migration. Local knowledge revealed the location of the roost sites, which tended to form in reedbeds and were often located over water, affording the birds protection from terrestrial predators which might target the roosting birds overnight.

I remember the regular visits to our local site, arriving before dusk to set the nets that we hoped would catch the birds as they came in to roost. We'd used a tape lure, broadcasting Swallow calls, to help pull the birds in. Once the nets were set, and the tape running, we'd retreat to a gateway a few hundred metres back from the nets to watch and wait. It was amazing to see the first Swallows arrive, the numbers gradually building until the birds were wheeling back and forth above the reedbed in a flock numbering several hundred individuals. Finally, as dusk fell the birds dropped from the sky and into the reeds, the nets catching a portion of those entering the roost. Being able to work the roost over several weeks, from late July to September, and with ringing sessions every seven to 10 days, we soon settled into a routine for setting the nets, catching, extracting and then processing the birds. The sessions continued until the birds had moved south, leaving the roost empty and with no new birds arriving from sites located further north. In one year, the arrival of a Hobby saw the birds leave to roost elsewhere, ending our season prematurely. Nevertheless, the project was a great success, generating over 32,000 captures of juvenile birds and 5,000 of adult birds from the 41 British and Irish roost sites alone.

An analysis of the British and Irish data set, led by Liz Coiffait in 2011, revealed that both adult and juvenile Swallows increased their body mass prior to migration. On average, adults gained more mass than juveniles and there was strong evidence that the increase in mass was a result of individuals building up their fat reserves in preparation for migration. Individuals caught at more southerly sites within Britain and Ireland had developed larger fat reserves than those caught further north, a pattern of increase similar to that noted for birds caught at sites in southern Europe. Interestingly, the level of fat reserves was less in the British and Irish birds than seen in southern Europe, suggesting that our birds were probably gaining sufficient fat reserves to enable them to cross to the Continent, where they would then presumably undergo further fattening before making a crossing of the Mediterranean. Examination of Swallows in Spain and Italy supported this, by finding that the amount of fat stored prior to migration varied according to the width of barrier that had to be crossed ahead of them. Fat loads of individuals caught at sites in Italy were almost two grams heavier than those caught in southern Spain, where the crossing of the Mediterranean is that much shorter. While Swallows have the opportunity to forage on the wing, perhaps such opportunities are reduced when the birds are crossing the sea or extensive areas of desert.

Another of our aerial feeders, the Swift, can leave the breeding grounds as early as mid-July, with adults typically beginning their migration just a few days after their chicks have fledged the nest. Departures tend to be early in years with good summer weather, but following poor weather, when the growth of nestling Swifts is much reduced and they spend far longer in the nest, adult birds may not leave until much later, perhaps as late as September. The young Swifts depart very soon after leaving the nest; in fact as Professor Chris Perrins notes, an individual from his study colony in Oxford left its nest box on 31 July and was found dead in Madrid just three days later, while it parents were still using the box for roosting.

From east to west

For many of us the spectacle of autumn migration, of birds leaving our shores, is captured in the flocks of Swallows and martins that gather on telegraph wires and fence lines from late summer. Many of our other migrants leave without us really noticing, and it is only when, as birdwatchers, we encounter 'falls' of migrants on the coast that the sense of movement is broadened to other species. Of course many of these birds, encountered on a damp morning and with winds coming in off the North Sea, will be birds from breeding populations located further north and east, drifted to our shores by the weather. They are not our birds, at least not in the sense of having bred here. Their arrival does, however, signal a key period in any birdwatcher's calendar, a period when eyes turn to the weather forecast and fingers are crossed in the hope of rarity and spectacle.

The autumn migration sees many birders head to the coast, with favoured sites regularly attracting significant crowds. Rarities do turn up; vagrants that have strayed from their normal migration route end up hundreds or even thousands of miles from where they should have been. While rarities provide the buzz that many birders seem to thrive on, for many others it is the broader supporting cast of species, and the sense of place, that have greater resonance. To be on the Norfolk coast before dawn on an October day, the overnight rain clearing off the back of a wind from the east, is to anticipate the spectacle of migration. At first it will be a small scatter of birds; a few Chiffchaff, Goldcrest or Blackcap perhaps, but then it might be a few dozen Redwing, Song Thrush or Blackbird, and slowly the numbers build, with Skylark and Meadow Pipit on the move overhead. As the light improves, so more and more birds appear from the hedgerows.

At certain sites, scattered around the coast, a network of bird observatories becomes the focus for many ringers and birdwatchers. The volunteers who manage these sites operate the ringing stations and look after visitors, contributing information on the numbers of birds passing through, their work adding to our understanding of migration patterns. We know, for example, that Pied Flycatchers from the populations breeding in the western half of Britain begin to turn up at our coastal bird observatories from August; sites in the south and west of the region see peak numbers in August, while sites further east see their peak numbers in early September. The observatory on Fair Isle, Shetland, sees its peak arrival later into September, suggesting that these are passage birds from the Scandinavian breeding populations. Pied Flycatchers from across the western European breeding range all appear to filter down into Spain and Portugal, from where they will make the crossing into Africa. The western breeding distribution within the UK also explains why it is our west coast bird observatories that see the bulk of our Pied Flycatchers during the autumn.

Photographs
Flight Lines trip to
Bardsey Bird Observatory

Greg Poole
Extracting a Goldcrest
Mixed media

Kim Atkinson
Processing a Coal Tit
Gouache

John Threlfall
Redstart studies
Pencil and watercolour

Bardsey Bird and Field Observatory

Out to the west, just a few kilometres off the southern tip of the Llyn Peninsula in North Wales is Ynys Enlli (Bardsey) – 'the island in the currents'. Home to a bird observatory since 1953, the island attracts birdwatchers, ringers and artists, including some of those involved in the Flight Lines project. An almost constant run of spring and autumn bird logs record the changing numbers of migrant birds passing through the island. Some of these will have been attracted to the island by the lighthouse, whose light has a range of over 46 km. The Bardsey light appears to attract migrant birds under fairly specific conditions, usually up to one week either side of the new moon and when weather conditions are conducive. On such occasions, birds attracted to the light fly continuously around until they find somewhere to land, collapse exhausted or collide with something. Erection of additional gantry lighting in 1998 has greatly reduced the problem.

In the second half of September 2015, three SWLA artists visited Bardsey as part of the Flight Lines project. The three, Kim Atkinson, Greg Poole and Darren Woodhead, arrived at a time when, unusually for Bardsey in September, there were relatively few migrant birds passing through. There were some, however. The small numbers of Goldcrests, Chiffchaffs and Robins entering the nets were ringed and processed by the observatory staff, providing a relaxed pace and the opportunity for the artists to sketch the ringers as they worked.

To compensate for the small influx of passerines, one of the assistant wardens took the artists with him as he went to check on the progress of the Manx Shearwater chicks nesting in his study burrows. While these amazing birds are not part of the Afro-Palearctic migration system they instead undertake an incredible migration, which sees them cross the Atlantic to winter off the coast of southern Brazil and Uruguay. Over the few days that the team of artists was on the island, they caught up with some of the migrants that would be wintering in Africa, including Wheatears. The passage of small birds would continue for some time after the team had returned to mainland; like the site at Icklesham in Sussex, where this chapter began, there would be a succession of species passing through until, finally, the last of our summer visitors had left our shores.

Personal Narrative

Carstramon Wood is a Scottish Wildlife Trust reserve in Dumfries and Galloway. Located in a beautiful oak woodland, the site hosts that celebrated trio of wet woodland migrants: Pied Flycatcher, Redstart and Wood Warbler. It also boasts the most spectacular swathe of Wild Hyacinth that I have ever seen, a sweet perfume that cannot fail but to breathe fresh life into you. I try to spend a few days here each spring, a place to sit and savour, but if I can get some sketches of these beguiling avian visitors at the same time then a real bonus is to be enjoyed.

It is a special place for me, as it is for members of the North Solway Ringing Group, who have monitored the Pied Flycatcher population here for the past 13 years. The birds use nestboxes and I joined up with the team in order to discover the stories behind some of the birds I was drawing. Their records show that the male flycatchers arrive during mid-April and, if such a thing as a normal year exists, then about 7–10 days later the females arrive.

After hatching, both parents enter the box to feed the young and this provides a chance to catch the ever wary males. By the second week the chicks are half way towards fledging and can be ringed. Records show fluctuations from year to year, the harsh effects of a cold wet spring and a lack of females in 2014 tempered by a best ever year in 2015, when I visited.

John Threlfall
SWLA Artist

The journey south

As the thousands of small birds leave our shores so it is the human communities further south in Europe who take a turn to host them as they journey towards Africa. The arrival of large numbers of migrant birds, perhaps grounded by adverse weather conditions, alerts birdwatchers, both local and visiting, to the migrants passing through. Much of the migration across Europe happens on a broad front and it is only where the birds gather to take advantage of particular feeding conditions or other opportunities that they attract attention. While some migrants may face the challenge of crossing the Alps, for most it is the Mediterranean Sea that provides the first substantial barrier to be crossed. At its western end the Mediterranean narrows at the Straits of Gibraltar, reducing the sea crossing that the birds face. Many migrant birds make for this point, while birds from breeding locations located further east across Europe may take a more easterly route, either down through Italy or via Greece and the Balkans.

The narrow crossing points at Gibraltar in the west and the Bosporus in the east are of particular importance for larger migratory species, like birds of prey and storks, which rely on thermals to help them make these sea crossings. It has been calculated that at least 200,000 birds of prey of 22 different species pass through southern Spain and Gibraltar during autumn migration. The crossing is dominated by Honey Buzzards and Black Kites, with in excess of 100,000 Honey Buzzards making the journey. However, these figures are dwarfed by the numbers of soaring birds passing through the Middle East, which probably exceed two million individuals and deliver a true wildlife spectacle for visiting birdwatchers.

Choosing a route

As we have already noted, the migratory journey presents a significant challenge for a small bird; indeed, it is thought that this is the stage of the cycle in which most of the annual mortality occurs in migrant land birds.

A migrating bird faces many threats, from predation and bad weather to a failure in navigation and starvation. The route taken and the timing of the journey may influence a bird's chances of success or failure. The route used will be influenced by the location of suitable wintering areas, by opportunities to refuel along the way, by the bird's capacity to store sufficient fat reserves, and by the predictability and timing of local weather conditions. Identifying the routes used by the different populations of a species, and understanding the risks associated with each of these, may help us to resolve the reasons behind the population declines evident in so many of our summer migrants.

Information on the routes used by migrating birds has traditionally come from direct observation – records of birds in particular localities – and through bird ringing. While these approaches can tell us a great deal, they can be misleading, perhaps because of biases in where birdwatchers (the observers) like to go on holiday or because of the geography of hunting pressure (ringed birds that have been shot may be more likely to be found and reported than those dying from natural causes).

Technological advances have seen the development of tiny tracking devices, from geolocators and radio-tags through to satellite-tags and others which tap in to the mobile phone network. Geolocators have been used on a number of our migrants; these devices record light levels, date and time; from this information it is possible to work out where the bird was on a given day, though with a varying degree of accuracy. Another downside of geolocators, and of other devices that store the information locally, is that the bird has to be recaptured in order for the data to be downloaded. This means that we only get information from those individuals that return successfully from their migration. Knowledge of where and when individuals die during migration may provide important evidence of the reasons for population declines and, additionally, also highlight where conservation action needs to be directed, perhaps through the protection of important stopover sites.

The development of tags that reveal their location – either via the mobile phone network or via earth-orbiting satellites – now allows us to follow the journeys of both the birds that succeed and those that fail. Knowing where a bird died, and when, can help reveal problems encountered on migration. If we can track a sufficient number of individuals from different parts of the breeding range, then we can determine whether different routes are used and, if so, whether the route selected might explain potential differences in population trend evident between regions. A good example of the value of this approach comes from recent BTO research into Cuckoo migration, delivered by researchers Chris Hewson and Phil Atkinson, working in the BTO's International Team.

Chasing Cuckoos

Monitoring of Cuckoo populations within the UK, through the BTO's core survey schemes, has revealed that the species is in rapid decline, its UK populations falling by 43% between 1995 and 2014. Interestingly, Cuckoo population trends vary in different parts of the UK, with populations across much of England declining strongly, while those in Scotland and parts of the western UK are stable or even increasing. The Cuckoos breeding in different parts of Britain may be using different habitats or even different host species, which may also have an influence on their population trend. However, use of BTO Nest Record Scheme and BTO/JNCC/RSPB Breeding Bird Survey data to examine whether the large-scale declines in Cuckoo populations are the result of changes in host species abundance, or the timing of their breeding attempts, suggest that these are not the primary drivers in the decline. While the availability of Dunnock nests has decreased, availability of Reed Warbler nests has increased, so perhaps the regional differences in fortunes are down to things happening elsewhere.

Chris Hewson and colleagues have been catching and tagging male Cuckoos since 2011, building up a picture of their movements. Until very recently, the tags used on Cuckoos were too big to be fitted to female Cuckoos – or to smaller males – limiting the early work to larger male birds. The team has tracked birds from nine widely spaced sites, which also vary in habitat type and, most likely, the host species used by the Cuckoos. One of the first discoveries to emerge from this work was that the birds use two different migration routes to reach the same wintering area. Some individuals use a western route, which takes them down through Spain, while others use an eastern route, which sees them leave Europe via Italy or the Balkans. All of the birds winter in Central Africa and, come spring, move into West Africa before returning to the UK, with most using the western route. That the birds use two different routes to reach the same wintering area is a novel and rather surprising finding.

All of the Cuckoos have to make a crossing of the Sahara, and the team has investigated the survival rates of birds during the different stages of their journey. Individual birds show a degree of consistency in their movements from one year to the next. Interestingly, the team found that survival through to completion of the desert crossing was significantly lower for those birds using the western route via Spain; this was despite the fact that this route is 12% shorter than the eastern one to this point. Examination of the locations where individual Cuckoos died, as revealed by a change in the information received from the tags, revealed that most of the excess mortality associated with the western route occurred within Europe at stopover sites in southern Europe. Decreasing rainfall in Spain, with associated wild fires and more frequent droughts, may be impacting the birds as they attempt to refuel

here, perhaps by removing or greatly reducing the availability of the caterpillars that they rely upon for food.

One of the most important aspects of this finding is the discovery that the proportion of birds within each of the nine study sites using the western route is correlated with the degree of decline seen in the local breeding population. Where a greater proportion of the individuals within a regional population use the western route, there is a more pronounced decline in the breeding population. This provides the first evidence that conditions during migration can influence the population dynamics of Cuckoos – or indeed any long-distance migrant – via effects on survival. It also shows that tracking devices can be used to identify areas critical to a species or a population. Such information can then inform conservation action, perhaps by providing evidence to support the designation of protected area status or by feeding into models that seek to predict the possible consequences of future changes in land use or climate.

Of course, this is only part of the UK Cuckoo story; we have yet to discover if female Cuckoos follow the same routes as the male birds. Since female Cuckoos leave later than the males, they could even use different stopover sites in order to make the most of seasonal changes in the abundance of favoured prey along their route. While adult Cuckoos of both sexes respond to tape playback – though females respond less readily than males – allowing them to be caught in mist nets and tagged, fitting tags to juvenile birds could be more of a challenge. This may mean that securing an understanding of how young Cuckoos migrate, and the routes that they take, is going to take somewhat longer.

Nightjars and Swifts

Tracking devices have also revealed the autumn migration of our Nightjars and Swifts, adding important information on species for which the reporting of ringed birds from overseas has been rather patchy. Our knowledge of the autumn migration of European Nightjars comes from recent studies using geolocators and GPS-tags, and involving birds from breeding populations in the UK, France, Belgium and southern Sweden. The autumn migration appears to be made across a broad front, with birds crossing the Mediterranean from southern Spain in the west, to Greece and, possibly, the Balkans in the east. Nightjars leave their UK breeding grounds in late August or early September, initially making a rapid movement to sites in southern Europe, where they can take on fuel before making a crossing of the Mediterranean. Once across and into North Africa they stop again, feeding up for a week or more before attempting a crossing of the Sahara.

While many small migrants can travel overnight and refuel during the day, nocturnal species like the Nightjar face the additional challenge of

Dafila Scott
Swifts over the fen
Pastel

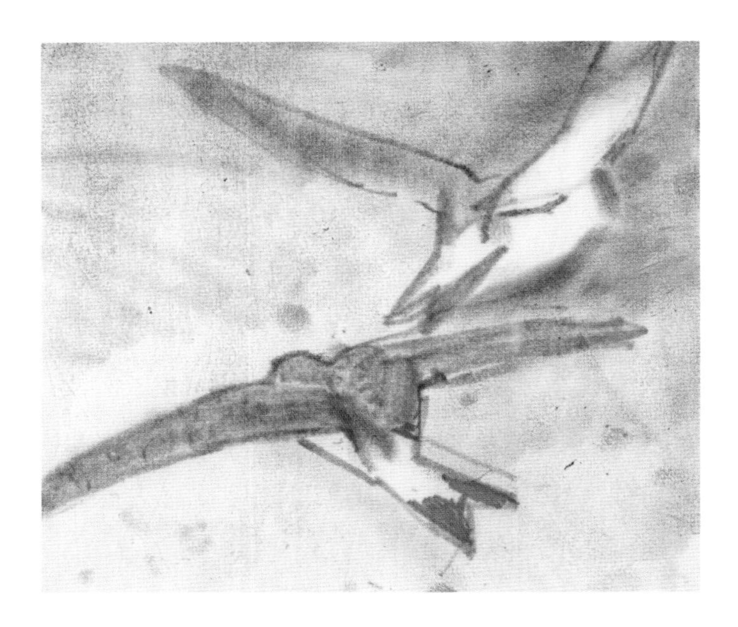

Matt Underwood
Flight study I
Monotype

Matt Underwood
Flight study II
Monotype

Matt Underwood
At the port
Monotype

how to allot their time when both activities happen during the hours of darkness. It seems likely that migrating Nightjars carry additional fat reserves during migration, providing them with some flexibility around refuelling opportunities. The information gained from the small number of individuals that have been tracked so far, suggests that Cameroon, Nigeria and Togo provide stopover sites for Nightjars that have made the desert crossing, allowing them to prepare for the final leg of their journey and the crossing of a final barrier, in the form of the central African tropical rainforest.

The final leg of the autumn migration for our Nightjars and its timing may well be related to the southward movement of the Inter Tropical Convergence Zone (ITCZ). The ITCZ is where the trade winds from the south-east and north-east converge to form a band of convective cloud, which drives the seasonal rains within the African tropics. The location of the ITCZ and its rain-bearing cloud has a pronounced influence on vegetation growth and the associated flush in invertebrate abundance that is so important to migrating and wintering birds. The ITCZ does not remain in one spot throughout the year, but moves north and south on a predictable basis. Its southward movement at the time when our Nightjars begin the final leg of their autumn migration may also provide them with a tailwind, aiding the journey south and seeing the birds reach wintering areas in the Democratic Republic of Congo and south to Namibia from late October onwards.

Swifts spend virtually all of their time on the wing, and it has long been assumed that they can feed as they go while on migration. That they spend so much of their life on the wing has provided little opportunity to build up a picture of where Swifts winter and the routes used to get there. When the BTO's Migration Atlas was published in 2002, presenting information from nearly 90 years of bird ringing, the maps for Swift showed just a scattering of dots in Africa, suggestive of a wintering range that extended from the Democratic Republic of Congo in Central Africa across to the Indian Ocean. Such static maps failed to reveal whether individual birds moved around during the winter months or even used different wintering areas in different years. As we will see later in this book, new technologies have greatly improved our knowledge of what our Swifts do once they reach Africa.

UK Swifts, tagged at their breeding colonies with geolocators, mostly leave the UK during the second half of July, something that is also reflected in the birdwatching records submitted through BirdTrack – a tool for birdwatchers to collate and share their birdwatching records. A typical geolocator track might see an individual leave the UK in the third week of July, spend a few days in Spain a week later and then reach Gambia on Africa's west coast during the first week of August. After a few days here the bird will then move across to Central Africa, a journey of some 10,000 kilometres completed in under a month.

From the western woods

Unlike the sparsity of ring-recovery information that we have for Nightjar, there is rather more information on the migration routes and wintering areas for some of our other summer visitors. Pied Flycatchers, for example, leave their British breeding grounds in August, the timing of departures influenced by the success of the breeding season and whether there are late young still in the nest. Information from the recoveries of ringed individuals, coupled with a small amount of information from birds fitted with geolocators, reveals the importance of south-western France, north-western Spain and northern Portugal for UK Pied Flycatchers, where they presumably fatten up in preparation for the next leg of their migratory journey. Here they are joined by birds from other western European breeding populations, which will also cross into Africa and, it appears, follow Africa's Atlantic coast south towards the wintering grounds. As noted above, ring-recoveries and tracking data also demonstrate an Iberian route for UK Swifts, which also follow the Atlantic coast before heading inland across the southern countries of West Africa towards wintering grounds in Central Africa.

We have relatively little information on the autumn journeys made by our breeding Redstarts, another of the migrants taking advantage of the nestboxes erected in our western oak woods. Redstarts leave their breeding sites during August and filter south, joining other individuals from the western European breeding populations at sites in France and Spain. The timing of this movement appears to be similar for both adult and juvenile birds. A passage of birds through eastern and southern England is evident later into the autumn and involves Scandinavian birds, presumably also heading towards Iberia. However, it is thought that some individuals from the Scandinavian breeding populations take a more easterly route, crossing the Mediterranean via Italy or the Balkans.

Geolocators have been used on a handful of Redstarts from Denmark, which used the western route to reach their African wintering grounds. Two relatively short stopovers were made by these birds, one in southern Europe or North Africa, and the second slightly further south but still prior to the desert crossing. The tracked birds appeared to continue south-west towards Africa's Atlantic coast before making a sharp turn east, taking them to wintering grounds in southern Mali and northern Burkina Faso. Whether British birds winter as far east as this is unknown, the only recoveries from south of the Sahara of ringed birds known to be part of the UK breeding population come from Senegal and Gambia. Interestingly, while one of these birds was caught in Gambia during October – and so may have still been on its autumn migration – the other two records, one each from Senegal and Gambia, come from January and February. Might these recoveries suggest that our birds winter at the western end of the wintering

Harriet Mead
Sawblade Nightjar
Welded found objects

range? Information from birdwatchers, coupled with that collected from across Europe's various bird ringing schemes, suggests that European Redstarts winter across the Sahel zone, from Senegal in the west to Eritrea in the east, and we might predict that birds that breed further west, such as in the UK, winter the furthest west. Arrivals in Senegal begin during early September but it is another month before peak numbers are reached, the birds favouring a mix of different habitats, from very dry scrub savannah to areas of well-established forest.

Other summer visitors, such as Whitethroat, Reed Warbler and Yellow Wagtail, also follow autumn migration routes that lead them into West Africa, but not every species does this. We have already seen that some of our Cuckoos take an eastern route, crossing the Mediterranean via Italy, Greece or the Balkans, and it appears that our Lesser Whitethroats do something similar. In the case of Lesser Whitethroat, it seems that the entire European breeding population moves south or south-east, converging in the Middle East and from there moves towards wintering areas in East Africa and central West Africa. A concentration of ring-recoveries in the north of Italy, coupled with knowledge of the fat loads of departing birds, suggests that Italy is an important stopover site for UK Lesser Whitethroats. The birds then move to Greece and it is from here that the Mediterranean is crossed, seemingly on quite a broad front. The use of this eastern route by some of our summer migrants potentially brings them into contact with hunters and trappers, operating in Italy, Malta, Egypt, Cyprus and elsewhere.

Hunting and the Mediterranean islands

The unregulated and illegal hunting of birds across the Mediterranean takes a significant toll on the migrants passing through the region during both autumn and spring passage. A 2015 report by BirdLife International put an estimate of 25 million birds on the numbers shot or trapped each year, with particularly large numbers of a few key species, such as Quail and Turtle Dove, taken annually. In terms of the geography of this illegal persecution, Egypt (5.7 million), Italy (5.6 million), Syria (3.9 million), Lebanon (2.6 million) and Cyprus (2.3 million) account for the lion's share. That Italy and Cyprus, both EU member states, should feature so prominently reveals the difficulties in implementing wildlife legislation where there is a long cultural history of hunting and illegal killing for both food and recreational purposes. Despite the existence of appropriate legislation within Italy, illegal hunting is a particular problem in Brescia province, within the Po Delta and on Sardinia, and remains a widespread activity more generally across the country.

The Mediterranean islands provide important stopover sites for migrating birds, and it is little wonder that the high levels of persecution seen on Malta and Cyprus should have attracted such high profile criticism. The Maltese islands provide a stepping stone for migrant birds and are of particular importance for larger species breaking their journey overnight or during periods of bad weather. Raptors are often targeted when they come in to roost for the evening; during spring, hunters use dogs and spotlights to flush roosting harriers from agricultural land so that they can be shot. More than 170 bird species use the Maltese islands during the migration period, with ring-recoveries revealing the origins of some of these birds as being from as far north as Finland and as far south as South Africa. Uncontrolled and illegal hunting is widespread in Malta, particularly on the main islands of Malta and Gozo, with nearly 11,000 registered hunters and trappers; many more remain unregistered.

As a member of the EU, Malta is bound by the Birds Directive, which prohibits spring hunting. However, such is the politicised nature of hunting in Malta that a referendum held in April 2015 saw a narrow majority in favour of spring hunting continuing. Hunting laws have been weakened repeatedly, and the pro-hunting lobby has been able to secure significant political support. Hunter densities, which are roughly 47 hunters or trappers per square kilometre of huntable land, have seen public land annexed and members of the public and tourists assaulted. There have been several high profile incidents involving illegal hunting, and many thousands of others are logged annually by BirdLife Malta.

Like Malta, Cyprus is a key stopover site for small birds making a crossing of the eastern Mediterranean. Arriving migrants tend to concentrate within particular parts of the island, a fact well known to the local hunters and something that has seen the Famagusta district – located at the eastern end of the island – labelled as the worst place in the Mediterranean for illegal killing of migrant birds. Because of its recent history Cyprus is an island with political sensitivities, which makes enforcement of existing laws forbidding trapping all the more problematic. Even the UK government, which has military bases in Akrotiri and Dhekelia, has found it difficult to tackle the illegal killing of birds on land under its control. The British Sovereign Base Areas have, however, adopted an action plan in an attempt to halt illegal killing, and efforts are underway to educate local children on the conservation value of migrant species. Many of the birds caught and killed are sold as delicacies for local consumption, with Blackcaps, Chiffchaffs and Lesser Whitethroats commonly taken for this reason.

The Middle East and North Africa

The nature of the political situation within countries like Syria, Libya, Lebanon and Egypt makes it unlikely that illegal hunting of migrant birds will end soon. However, BirdLife partners and local agencies are working to understand the scale of the problem within some of these countries and to

Photographs
Springwatch camp, Malta
David Tipling/NaturePL

Spring Watch
Malta 2013

PULIZIJA

Hunters
set sights
on more
targets

BirdLife
MALTA
www.birdlifemalta.org

identify the underlying causes. A socioeconomic study of bird hunting along Egypt's Mediterranean coast, for example, has been a major step forward in this respect. The study, carried out by Dr Salwa Elhalawani, with support from Nature Conservation Egypt, BirdLife International and the Africa-Eurasian Migratory Waterbird Agreement organisation (AEWA), has sought to understand the communities and individuals involved in illegal hunting and their motivations. The hunting of birds has a very long history within Egypt and is considered both as a source of employment and of protein.

A range of methods are used to catch migrating birds in Egypt, with 'trammel' nets perhaps the most visible of these. The nets, which are erected on the coast in long lines, catch migrant birds as they arrive on the Mediterranean's southern shore, exhausted after a substantial sea crossing. Each set of nets tends to be family-owned, the section of coast on which the nets are erected passed from one generation to the next. Despite a system of hunting permits, and of laws governing where nets may be placed and how they should be spaced, these are not enforced. Other birds are caught using Mansaabs – tent-like structures of grass and sticks, which attract ground-dwelling birds like Quail and Corncrake, Ebs – large mist nets placed over trees, and lime sticks – though this is an uncommon and rather localised practice in Egypt.

Egyptian hunters used to service European markets for Quail, with an estimated 1–2 million birds exported into Europe between 1906 and 1913. They are now responding to new markets for migrant birds, both live and dead, opening up elsewhere. Hundreds of thousands of birds are now collected from Egypt's bird markets by traders who export them en masse, supplying a growing demand from countries in the Arabian Gulf. Birds of prey, particularly falcons for use in hunting, are also taken for export to these countries. The trade in migrant birds from Egypt is estimated to be worth up to $50,622,000 annually, although this figure is based on a local estimate of 11.8 million birds taken annually, which is double that presented by BirdLife in their 2015 report.

Those involved in bird hunting within Egypt fall into one of three categories: those who hunt for cultural or recreational reasons, those who hunt for subsistence, and those who hunt commercially. A high proportion of the hunters are from poor or marginalised communities, often supplementing income from other sources – such as fishing. It is the traders who profit most from hunting activity. Culturally, most Egyptians have a rather exploitative or consumptive view of the natural world, with birds in particular viewed as a resource rather than something to be conserved. Most of those interviewed by Salwa Elhalawani recognised that bird numbers were declining, particularly so over recent years, but many held the view that Allah would protect and secure sufficient birds for future generations.

Understanding these cultural attitudes, together with socioeconomic factors like the supporting contribution of hunting income to that derived from fishing, should help Egyptian conservation organisations to structure action plans to support a move away from hunting, at least for those who participate for subsistence, recreational or cultural reasons. Tackling those who hunt commercially to take advantage of markets elsewhere may require a different approach.

The impact of hunting

There is no doubt that the illegal hunting of birds migrating between Europe and Africa is a problem, but its impact at the population level is almost impossible to quantify. We just do not have the data that we need. Despite the numbers of birds being killed on their autumn migration, it is theoretically possible that this level of mortality might be compensated for by a density-dependent reduction in mortality on the wintering grounds. Put simply, with fewer birds present on the wintering grounds, competition for food resources should be reduced and overwinter mortality should fall. Of course, we do not know whether there is competition for food on the wintering grounds, nor is the density-dependent argument as strong during the spring migration through the Mediterranean. What is clear, however, is that efforts should be made to understand the impact of illegal hunting on declining species like Turtle Dove and other species of high conservation concern. Tackling illegal or unregulated hunting also requires an understanding of the communities involved in hunting and trapping; as the work in Egypt has demonstrated, communities may hunt for very different reasons, not all of which can be tackled with the same approach.

Smaller
turtle dove
shot a killed
at

Personal Narrative

A lot of shooting from close by. A number of men on the slope opposite, which is rocky, and has a number of square 'hides' as well as drystone terraces, and piled stones which are stands for bird-traps.

One of the hunters is in a tiny walled enclosure, half a mile away below us. It's the guy with glasses, combats and baseball cap, a liver and white speckled dog, red fourtrack; we saw him yesterday at the Turtle Dove shoot at Gudja. He goes off with the dog, casting around for a Quail he has shot.

In the drawing, the strong graphite marks represent shots, the sequences of little circles are Quail calls, but these could be from taped decoys. It's a drawing of the terrain dominated by sound. I did it when it wasn't my turn to note down gunshot – our job was to enumerate all shots heard as well as other details – and the data were then used to match up the hunters' claimed bag for the duration of the open season with their actual shooting rate, target species and so on.

We also called the police in when there were transgressions. One such was a lad who was filmed by one of the volunteers shooting at a Golden Oriole. Even though he admitted to being the subject of the film, in which the Golden Oriole could clearly be seen to be shot at (this one got away), still he denied he ever shot at illegal species; the police gave him his gun back and he strolled back along the track.

Kim Atkinson
Spring Watch Camp 2013, BirdLife Malta.

Breaking the journey

We have already seen how most migrant birds break their journeys into a number of distinct stages, halting to feed and to replenish the fat stores expended during the periods of sustained flight. Such breaks are known as 'stopovers' and they often take place ahead of crossing a significant barrier, such as the Mediterranean or the Sahara. Where birds stop and when will be influenced by a range of different factors.

Where and when to stop

Migration theory, based on the energetics of flight, suggests that small birds should divide their time while on migration between active flight and the use of stopover sites according to a ratio of roughly 1:7, which should see individuals spending about 85% of their time at stopover sites. The trade off between having sufficient fuel and not carrying too much weight dictates refuelling decisions, though of course these are also shaped by the distribution of feeding opportunities along the way. Small birds, on autumn migration, will tend to make a series of short 'hops' when moving across terrain in which feeding opportunities are readily available. Longer flights are made across inhospitable terrain, such as the sea or a desert. Time pressures, which come from the nature of the annual cycle, also have a role to play. Autumn migration tends to be more leisurely; the breeding season is over and there is less pressure to be somewhere else. Spring migration is more rapid, driven by the selection pressure that favours early arrival on the breeding grounds and the associated access to the best breeding territories and mates.

The habitats used by species during their migratory journeys may differ from those used during the breeding season, though many seem rather similar. In part this reflects the geography of where the species is, and the habitats actually available at a particular location. However, there will also be an element of selection, with migrating birds potentially responding to the availability of prey. In temperate latitudes we see a decline in invertebrate abundance in many more open habitats as autumn progresses and this may force some birds to move into those habitats where prey can still be found. We know, from work carried out close to Lake Constance in Germany, that warblers and Redstarts migrating through a site over the course of the autumn switch their foraging away from open shrubby habitats into areas of either denser scrub (Blackcap and Garden Warbler) or reedbed (Willow Warbler, Chiffchaff and Redstart). Resident birds, like Wrens and Dunnocks, also appear to make this switch.

Southern Spain and Portugal hold important stopover sites for birds migrating through the western end of the Mediterranean while, as we have seen, northern Italy (including the Po Watershed) may be important for birds taking a more easterly route. Earlier in the book we learned how our Reed Warblers and Sedge Warblers may adopt different strategies as they move south and refuel along the way – Sedge Warblers appear to use stopover sites that are widely spaced, a somewhat different approach to that favoured by migrating Reed Warblers. Interestingly, those Reed Warblers making the southwards journey later into the autumn appear to adopt an approach closer to that used by migrating Sedge Warblers, suggesting either that the time pressures evident later in the season influence the decisions made about where and when to refuel, or that the distribution of the resources needed by the birds has changed.

Departure date can also influence the timing of moult. Many migrants won't begin their annual moult until they are on the wintering grounds, or at least have crossed the Sahara. Stable isotope analysis, which can reveal where birds have replaced their feathers, shows that European House Martins use discrete moulting areas within Africa. Some species may initiate moult ahead of departure; in the case of Whitethroat, for example, the adults undertake a complete moult from early July and most will have finished this before they leave. Some, however, interrupt the moult of their primary or secondary feathers to begin the first leg of the southwards migration, the new feathers evident alongside older feathers when the birds are captured at stopover sites in southern Europe.

From Portugal to Italy

Spend time in southern Europe during the autumn migration period and you will encounter birds passing through on their journey south. By visiting important stopover sites, particularly those used by migrating waders or wildfowl, you will secure a sense of the sheer numbers of birds involved and see how the wave of migrants moves across Europe. The passage of Grasshopper Warblers, for example, through stopover sites in Portugal, which takes place during September and October, comes roughly a month after the peak passage seen at south coast sites in England. Coupled with a small number of ring-recoveries from the south-west of France, this suggests that the southward migration of Grasshopper Warbler is, at least initially, a rather protracted affair. A study of the birds using these Portuguese sites shows that some individuals have sufficient reserves to make a crossing of the Sahara direct from Portugal, but the greater proportion don't, implying that most need to fuel at sites further south, most likely in Morocco. The main arrival of Grasshopper Warblers at sites to the south of the Sahara, such as Djoudj in Senegal, occurs in early December which, coupled with the dates of the passage through Portugal, also adds weight to undiscovered stopover sites in Morocco or elsewhere within the north-west of Africa. The birds may also take the opportunity to undergo a complete moult of their flight feathers during this period, so there is still much to be discovered about the migration behaviour of this and other species.

The western parts of Spain and Portugal may be of particular importance for migrating Pied Flycatchers and Tree Pipits, in some cases with a concentration of ring-recoveries supporting the small amount of information being generated from geolocators and other tracking devices. Further east, some of our breeding Cuckoos use stopover sites situated within the Po Watershed, which encompasses the south and east facing slopes of the Alps, the northern Apennines, the Po Valley itself and the Po Delta. From the satellite data it appears that the Cuckoos are either using high altitude sites, made up of a mosaic of grass, scrub and forest patches, or sites associated with the Po River. Interestingly, the high altitude mosaic habitats are similar in many ways to the habitats being used by our Cuckoos in Spain.

As part of the BTO/SWLA Flight Lines project BTO Senior Research Ecologist Chris Hewson visited the Po Watershed in the company of Federico Gemma, an Italian artist who is also a member of the SWLA. Over the course of several days in July 2015 Chris and Federico visited a number of the stopover sites used by satellite-tracked Cuckoos from the UK breeding population. Federico's watercolours capture the habitats and localities at which the birds stopped, often for several days, providing Chris with an opportunity to speculate on why the sites might be favoured by the migrating birds. Was there a particular abundance of the caterpillars that feature so prominently in Cuckoo diet, or was there something else attracting them to the region? Chris suspects that the sites, which combine the right woodland mosaic habitats within a landscape with a good water supply, provide good foraging conditions for Cuckoos seeking to fatten up.

That there were Cuckoos here was in no doubt; Chris took an audio device with him, from which he was able to broadcast the familiar notes of a calling Cuckoo. These prompted male Cuckoos to come and investigate the source of the sound, leaving Chris to ponder on whether these were perhaps UK birds or, more likely, local birds. The combination of habitats available in relatively close proximity (the high altitude grassland, scrub and forest, together with patchy woodland in the valley), the water draining off the mountains and the fact that this area lies in a strategic location for UK Cuckoos heading off south-east, could account for its use. It is a high quality but not unique area that is strategically placed for 'our' birds, which explains why Cuckoos from Scandinavia and Germany do not appear to stop here.

The important role of the Po Watershed for UK Cuckoos, migrating south via the eastern route, can be seen from the autumn migrations of the tagged birds. The Po Watershed has been used as a stopover in each year of the BTO Cuckoo Tracking Project. In 2015, however, the area was hit by drought, prompting two of the Cuckoos to push further east, into Croatia. Over the following days, as the Cuckoos moved into Africa and began their crossing of the Sahara, we saw the loss of several birds. Had the drought reduced feeding opportunities to the extent that the birds were unable to fuel sufficiently to make the desert crossing? A similar problem, in the form of a severe drought in southern Spain, has had equally severe consequences for the birds using the western route in recent years.

The Alps of northern Italy may also be important for migrating Lesser Whitethroats and there is certainly a clustering of ring-recoveries from the region that might support such a view. Further south within Italy, a cluster of Wood Warbler recoveries suggest another stopover area important for UK migrants taking an eastern route. As more information is gained through the use of tracking devices, so more stopover sites may come to light, increasing the knowledge on which conservation decisions may be based.

Into Africa

Some of the birds crossing the Mediterranean may make another stopover once they have reached North Africa. The lower human population densities within this region, compared with southern Europe, means fewer ring-recoveries and a lack of information flowing from birdwatchers and local communities. As we have seen for Grasshopper Warbler, it is thought that there may be important stopover sites to the north of the Sahara, within Africa, awaiting discovery. However, knowledge of the migration strategies adopted by many of our migrant species, coupled with that on fat reserves and flight range, suggest that many autumn migrants fly direct from sites located to the north of the Mediterranean to others that lie to the south of the Sahara in what is known as 'sub-Saharan Africa'. Although we refer to these as direct flights, individuals birds probably do stop, but not for substantial periods and certainly not for several days at a time. In view of this knowledge, it seems likely that North Africa is more important as a stopover site during the spring migration, rather than during the autumn.

Photographs
Chasing Cuckoos on the Po Watershed

Garzaia di S.Alessandro
Ontaneto
Pioppeto coltivato
Acqua libera
Zona a canneti di Salicone
BENVENUTI
alla Garzaia
di S.Alessandro

08/07/2015 - Nei dintorni di Pizzighettone
Tra i campi di mais nelle zone del cuculo "Peckham".
Al primo tentativo appare un cuculo in volo per pochi secondi. Sono circa le 6,30 di mattina

Federico Gemma
Bee-eaters
Pencil and watercolour

Il bosco misto frequentato dal cuculo 'Cookie' all'interno del Monumento Naturale Garzaia di Sant'Alessandro in Provincia di Pavia - 9 luglio 2015 -
Federico Gemma

Sul greto del fiume, parzialmente in secca
qualche pescatore
sfida il caldo -
intorno tantissimi
gabbiani comuni e
garzette -

Federico Gemma 2015

Federico Gemma
Near Pavia
Watercolour

Federico Gemma
Fishermen
Pencil and watercolour

preparazione
dell'esca
gabbiani comuni
adulti e giovani

The Sahara

The Sahara desert presents a significant barrier to small migrating birds. Not only does the desert lack the vegetation that might support invertebrates for refuelling, it is also hot and dry, with these inhospitable conditions extending over some 2,000 km or more. A long-held view was that migrating songbirds should cross the desert in a single non-stop flight, since to stop in the desert to rest would expose individual birds to hot and dry conditions that would be fatally damaging to energy and water reserves. Most small birds migrate at night, stopping during the day to rest and feed, so the adoption of a non-stop flight across the desert would, it seem, require a change in behaviour.

Unsurprisingly perhaps, little information is available on bird movements within the vast desert landscape and the reports of birds occasionally observed in the desert were traditionally viewed as being individuals that had somehow failed in their migration, doomed to die. However, a few trapping studies carried out at desert oases have found the birds caught to be in generally good body condition and able to continue their migration after sunset. This hints, for some species at least, at a strategy for crossing the Sahara based around nocturnal flight and daytime rest, something referred to as intermittent migration, rather than a direct non-stop flight.

In 2007, Heikki Schmaljohann, from the Swiss Ornithological Institute, published a paper which provided support for intermittent migration in those birds making a crossing of the Sahara. Using a sophisticated radar system at three sites within the desert, Schmaljohann and colleagues recorded the timing and volume of migrating birds passing overhead. They hypothesised that if migrant birds broke their journey by resting in the desert during the day, they would see a peak in migrant passage soon after sunset, while if the birds flew non-stop the passage would be more equally spread throughout the whole day.

Schmaljohann's results were striking; across all of the three sites, each of which was surrounded by at least 300 km of vegetation-free desert, songbird migration increased significantly immediately after sunset, remaining high throughout the night and then decreasing after sunrise – abruptly so in autumn, but more gradually during spring. These small birds were resting in the desert during the day, and migrating at night. What the birds were not doing, however, was refuelling, so in a nutritional or energetic sense the journey was still being made in a single flight.

The difference in activity after dawn between spring and autumn could be related to the prevailing conditions and a decision to continue migration under favourable circumstances. During autumn, the small birds crossing the Sahara are aided by the trade winds, which provide a tail wind to those migrating south. The radar results showed that autumn movements were mostly made at altitudes of below a kilometre above the ground, where temperatures were typically between 25 and 35°C during the day, with humidities at or below 30%. These are challenging conditions, likely to increase water loss, which may be why the birds land and sit it out until sunset. During spring, migrating birds crossing the western Sahara are again aided by a tail wind – this time the anti-trade winds present at this time. Unlike in autumn, however, the radar revealed that the birds flew at higher altitudes – typically 2–4 km above the ground, where the temperature (at 10° C) and humidity (c.40%) would have been more favourable. Under such conditions, there may be more opportunity for individual birds to continue their migration into the daylight hours. There is more urgency to the spring migration than that seen in autumn, and it is this that might prompt birds to extend their migratory flights beyond dawn and into the start of the day.

Of course, these results also raise the question of why not simply fly higher during the desert crossing rather than attempt to break the journey and face the challenging desert conditions. There is evidence for the Cuckoo tracking work that UK Cuckoos do make the crossing in a single flight, travelling at altitude where the conditions are favourable.

One of the most interesting aspects of how individual birds make the journey south is in the use of particular routes and stopover sites. The geography of Europe and Africa, with the associated distribution of different habitats and feeding opportunities, will shape migration strategies at a broad scale, hence the concentration of species at those points where the crossing of the Mediterranean is at its narrowest, and the numbers of birds skirting the western edge of the Sahara, close to the Atlantic coast. Historical factors must also play a significant role too.

Away from the geographical constraints are differing patterns in fuelling strategies and in the distances individual species can cover with a given fuel load. Below this are the differences within a species, most of which are likely to be linked to breeding population, such that UK Lesser Whitethroats stopover in Italy while those from further north and east in Europe stopover in the Middle East. As we have seen for UK Cuckoos, there may even be differences within a population, differences so pronounced that while one individual may migrate south through Spain, another may go via Italy, but with both ending up on the same Central African wintering grounds.

Personal Narrative

Flying into Verona airport gives a Cuckoo's-eye view of the Po Watershed. To the north, the foothills of the Alps rise into distant mountains and to the south lies the north end of the Apennines, Italy's backbone. The area between these two sets of high peaks, encompassing the slopes of both sets of mountains and the 100 km wide floodplain between them, is an apparent goal area for many Cuckoos travelling between the UK and Central Africa.

Early July is the time for these birds to fatten on copious caterpillars, preparing for a gruelling crossing of the Mediterranean Sea and Sahara desert which would take them to wet-season Chad for a well-earned rest before heading south into the Congo rainforest. As I stepped off the plane to begin my own stay here, I was met by Federico Gemma, the artist with whom I was to document this important stopover.

With Federico Gemma I had the opportunity to travel along the length of the River Po, from the famous delta to the river's source 400 km away, high in the western Alps against the French border. But this year the Po was greatly diminished. From 2011 to 2014, Cuckoos stopping off in the Po watershed had without exception survived to continue their migrations and most had made it safely across the Sahara. Those stopping off in Spain had, in contrast, often struggled. This year the tables, if not quite turned, had at least evened up and we lost Cuckoos in the Po region for the first time. Nothing, it seems, is constant for these birds, their resourcefulness and population resilience constantly challenged by the shifting sands of climate and other environmental factors.

Chris Hewson
BTO Senior Research Ecologist

The wintering grounds

The Palearctic migrants arriving to winter in Africa make up 5–10% of the bird population present at this time of the year. While this is a relatively small percentage, it is important to realise that the arriving birds are not distributed evenly throughout the continent but instead favour particular regions, bioclimatic zones and habitats. The few studies examining the densities and distribution of migrant birds in Africa suggest that they can form a significant component of the avifauna at some sites. Work in northern Nigeria and Senegal has shown migrant warblers to be roughly twice as common as their African counterparts, though only half as common as other African birds within the same guild of arboreal insect-feeders. Within reedbed habitat in northern Nigeria, three European *Acrocephalus* warblers (Reed Warbler, Sedge Warbler and Great Reed Warbler) were found to be four times as numerous as the three African species (African Reed Warbler, Lesser Swamp Warbler and Rufous Swamp Warbler).

There is good evidence from an increasing number of studies that the use of a particular wintering area can influence survival rates and other key demographic parameters. We know, for example, that weather conditions influence the survival of many small migrant birds. Such effects can either be direct, where weather conditions fatally force migrants off course, or indirect, where they determine the amount of food available on the wintering grounds. Rainfall appears to be of particular importance, shaping the amount of invertebrate food available within Africa, and rainfall patterns within the Sahel region of West Africa have been shown to exert a larger and more consistent influence on the survival of species breeding in western Europe than conditions further north in Africa or within Europe itself. Such impacts are not just felt by birds like Whitethroat and Sedge Warbler, which winter in the Sahel, they are also felt by those species, such as Reed Warbler and Garden Warbler, wintering further south in the humid zone but which pass through the Sahel on migration.

The Sahel

The importance of the Sahel to migrant birds comes from its location. It is the first place to refuel after crossing the Sahara desert during autumn migration, and provides wintering habitat and food for a number of Afro-Palearctic migrants. Although subject to a number of different definitions, roughly speaking the Sahel is the region of West Africa that sits between the Sahara (to the north) and the wetter Guinea zone (to the south). When considering those migrants which breed in Britain and Ireland, it is the western end of the Sahel, extending from Senegal in the west to Niger in the east, that is of most relevance, since this is where many of our birds winter. Another defining characteristic of the Sahel is its low rainfall; with a long-term average rainfall of between 200–600 mm this is a semi-arid region, prone to drought. The broader 'arid zone' within which the Sahel sits also includes the Sudan savannahs, and it is within this broader area that species like Whitethroat, Lesser Whitethroat, Sedge Warbler and Sand Martin.

Although nearly 70 different avian migrants are known to use the region, it is the Whitethroat that brought this part of Africa to the attention of British birdwatchers, conservation practitioners and academics studying bird populations. In 1974, a paper by Derek Winstanley, Bob Spencer and Ken Williamson appeared in the BTO's journal Bird Study, posing the question 'Where have all the Whitethroats gone?'. This paper revealed that between the 1968 and 1969 breeding seasons the British Whitethroat population had crashed, falling by a staggering 77% according to figures from the BTO's core monitoring scheme at that time – the Common Birds Census. The population crash was not just limited to Britain; figures from the ringing station on the German island of Helgoland, for example, reported that just 77 Whitethroats were caught on migration in 1969 compared with 614 the previous year. Evidence from the BTO's Ringing Scheme and Nest Record Scheme highlighted that the 1968 breeding season had been a successful one, suggesting that the cause of the sudden decline lay elsewhere, either along the migration routes or on the wintering grounds.

Winstanley et al.'s paper investigated a number of possibilities, before presenting evidence that a change in rainfall patterns on the Sahelian wintering grounds had precipitated the crash. The 1968 rainfall figures for the region as a whole were down by a quarter on the long-term average, with some areas experiencing rainfall levels as much as 70% below normal. Migrant birds, reaching the Sahel in late autumn, arrive at the end of the wet season and face six months of deteriorating conditions and, presumably, a dwindling abundance of favoured foods. The critical period for those birds using the area will be the few weeks immediately prior to the spring crossing of the Sahara; this is when birds will need to lay down the fuel reserves required for the next stage of their journey north.

The prolonged period of drought which followed the 1968/69 event, with rainfall well below the long-term average, was associated with significant declines in the breeding populations of those migrant species using Sahelian open grassland

and dry farmland habitats. These declines, which took place between 1970 and 1990, were then followed by significant declines in other migrant birds, this time those associated with more structurally complex habitats containing a greater proportion of tree and shrub cover. While the deep-rooted shrub and woody plants may have been more resilient than the shallow-rooted grasses, and so been less impacted initially by the drought, this is not the whole story. For Whitethroat, we have seen the partial recovery of our UK breeding population since the low point witnessed in the mid-1980s – the Common Birds Census/Breeding Bird Survey index increasing by 72% between 1989 and 2014 – but breeding numbers today are still less than half of what they were in 1968.

Redstart was another of the species whose population showed a decline following the Sahelian drought. Redstarts wintering in the region favour arid and semi-arid landscapes, utilising dry *Acacia* scrub, woodland of various types and the edges of cultivated ground. Within these dry habitats they forage on the ground, taking ground-dwelling invertebrates such as ants, which may allow them to exploit opportunities that are not available to leaf-gleaning species later in the winter period because of the drying conditions and lack of the new growth required by leaf-feeding insects. Redstart populations have increased over recent years, largely driven by a sharp upturn in fortunes within Wales, but the UK breeding range is still a third smaller than it was at the time of the BTO's first Atlas of Breeding Birds, published in 1976. More widely, numbers have been increasing across Europe, particularly so since 2005, which might suggest improving conditions on the wintering grounds.

Work by Stephen Baillie and Will Peach, using data from the Ringing Scheme, Nest Record Scheme and the Common Birds Census, showed fluctuations in the losses of adult Sedge Warblers and Whitethroats to be correlated with Sahelian rainfall, through its effects on vegetation and invertebrate abundance. Work within the region, most notably that carried out by Jared Wilson, Matt Stevens and Will Cresswell, has revealed interesting associations between wintering Whitethroats and habitat features, including the number, size and density of trees. While Whitethroats can make use of even very degraded habitats, certain trees, such as *Salvadora persica* – whose fruit are used for pre-migratory fattening – appear to be of particular significance. Understanding the habitat requirements of species on their wintering grounds may be of real importance, not least because of the changes that we have seen in the Sahel landscape since the 1968 drought.

Changing land use

Although devastating at the time, the Sahel drought is probably not the most important factor in the long-term decline of migrant birds using the region. The partial return of the rains has seen a period of rapid 'greening' of vegetation and growth in the human population. This greening, evident in the images remotely sensed from satellites orbiting the earth, is not the natural vegetation cover returning; instead, it reflects a period of agricultural intensification, supported by a growing number of irrigation projects and an increasing reliance on introduced or economically important agricultural species. Woody vegetation has been lost, either over-harvested for timber and firewood, overgrazed by increasing densities of livestock or replaced by forest monocultures. Two consequences of these changes have been the loss of biodiversity and a boom in agricultural and economic progress. In general, the human population growth rate within the Sahel has averaged just over 3% per year since 1970, equivalent to a doubling of the population in just 23 years. The change in land use within the region has been significant, something that has also had an impact on tree density (down 82%), with declines in the numbers and diversity of native birds, especially birds of prey, and large mammals also evident.

Changing land use has also had a pronounced impact on waterbirds, including migratory species like Ruff and Garganey. The Sahel was well-known for its ephemeral wetlands and for the thousands of temporary pools that formed wherever the seasonal rains collected. Many of these pools have been lost to land drainage, irrigation and water control projects, built since the 1970s and linked to the process of agricultural intensification. The pools and other areas of wet or flooded ground are also important for aerial feeders, such as Sand Martin, which take advantage of the small flies and other insects often associated with such waterbodies.

Various studies have linked Sahel rainfall with the survival rates of the Sand Martins wintering in the area, with both adult and juvenile survival significantly improved during wet years. Drought conditions appear to put significant strain on wintering Sand Martins, with ringing studies suggesting a selection pressure towards smaller body size during drought years. There is also evidence of competition between individual Sand Martins for food under drought conditions, with David Norman and Will Peach finding that adult survival was linked to the size of the Sand Martin population breeding within Europe and suggestive of density dependent competition for limited resources on the wintering grounds.

Impacts on wintering migrants have been documented by in excess of 70 different studies, highlighting how changing ecological conditions within the Sahel have affected the survival rates, migration phenology and even the breeding success of species which use the area as part of their annual migratory cycle. The recent greening of the Sahel, while viewed as a political, agricultural and economic success by many, has had profound consequences for biodiversity; it is a pattern likely to be repeated elsewhere within Africa, as land use changes are delivered to meet the increasing demands of a growing human population. There is a risk for us humans in developing the Sahel in this way, for even with the introduction of new

Bruce Pearson
Senegal shoreline
Relief print

irrigation schemes we cannot escape the fact that the Sahel is a semi-arid ecosystem. As a consequence, it is inherently less stable than other eco-regions and far less resilient to some of the changes that we might expect to see under future climatic scenarios.

The spatial pattern of these changes in land use is complex, as are the politics of the region. While most of the Sahelian countries are signatories to international conventions related to conservation, these have to be considered alongside other policy priorities, such as addressing the welfare of the people who live within the region. The underlying poverty seen within this part of Africa very quickly relegates conservation priorities, such that they can only be considered when viewed as components of wider development strategies that target poverty, welfare and quality of life. Identifying strategies that sustain, rather than damage, those habitats of importance to native and migrant species will require conservationists to work closely with planners, economists and others. It will also require substantially more evidence on the ecology and habitat requirements of migrants wintering within the Sahel, and that will require financial support and the transfer of skills and expertise to a new generation of researchers and conservation practitioners working within the region.

Beyond the Sahel

The Sahel is an important part of our migration story, but it is not the only part of the vast African continent to be used by birds that breed here in Britain and more broadly across Europe. While Reed Warblers, Garden Warblers and Willow Warblers may pass through the area they actually overwinter within Africa's humid zone. It has been shown by Ali Johnston, working at the BTO, that average estimates of annual adult survival are significantly higher for species wintering within the humid zone compared with those wintering within the arid zone. The arid zone is less stable climatically and, as we have seen, is an area where there have been significant changes in land use over recent years.

The small numbers of recoveries of ringed birds from elsewhere within Africa have long-hinted that some of our migrants move further south and east across the African continent. It has long been known, for example, that UK Swallows – the icon of the northern summer – winter in South Africa. The first record of a UK Swallow wintering in South Africa came in December 1912, when an adult female, ringed at a nest in Staffordshire by James Masefield – brother of the poet John Masefield – was found in Natal Province, just two days before Christmas. Since then, more than 400 UK Swallows have been recaptured in South Africa at winter roosts. In addition, several dozen Swallows ringed in South Africa have been recovered here in the UK. South African studies have also helped to reveal what the Swallows using the roosts do during the day; it seems that most of the birds using a roost remain faithful to it throughout the winter months and forage within about 50 km of the site. Information from bird ringing suggests that UK Swallows winter across South Africa but it does appear that our birds tend to be more common in the western part of the country, with birds from further east within Europe becoming more common as you move east within South Africa towards the Indian Ocean. A paucity of ring-recoveries from elsewhere within Africa means our understanding of the migration routes and other sites used by the Swallows as they journey across the African continent is less well known. This is something that we have recently been able to address for another aerial feeder, the Swift.

Swifts and wider movements

That Swifts spend so much of their life on the wing means that we have, until recently, had a poor understanding of where they wintered and how they got there. As with some of our other summer migrants, the advent of data loggers, geolocators and other tracking devices has revolutionised our understanding over the last few years. Geolocators monitor light intensity at regular intervals and record this alongside the date and time of the observation. By using the timing of dawn and dusk to estimate longitude, and daylight length to estimate latitude, this combination of information can then provide a location for the bird – though admittedly with less accuracy than that achievable with GPS-tags.

Since the summer of 2010 the BTO has fitted a number of Swifts with geolocators – part of a wider project on the species – in the hope of revealing more detail on Swift migration. The results of this work can be neatly summarised by looking at the movements of an individual bird, known as A320. This Swift was fitted with a geolocator overnight on 21/22 July 2010 at a site in Cambridgeshire. When it was recaptured the following year, the data collected by the tag revealed an incredible journey. A320 had left Britain a few days after being tagged, arriving in Spain in the last week of the month and then crossing into North Africa, before moving quickly south to spend several days in Gambia during the first week of August. Just over a week later it was in the Democratic Republic of Congo, where it remained from 17 August through until 9 December. At this point A320 moved south-east, spending the rest of December and most of January in two different areas within Mozambique, close to the Indian Ocean. Other UK Swifts fitted with tags show a similar pattern, moving to Central Africa, from which additional late winter movements are then made.

The movements made by A320 reveal three new pieces of information: that autumn migration involves a western route that follows the Atlantic seaboard of West Africa; that the wintering area extends from Central Africa

Greg Poole
Yellow Wagtail
Gouache

Greg Poole
Sand Martins
Gouache

down to Mozambique; and that there is an important spring stopover site in Liberia – about which we will learn more in a later chapter. Studies of Swedish and German Swifts have revealed the importance of the Congo Basin as a wintering area, so it is interesting that British Swifts – and some German birds – appear to range over a broader area during the winter months. Of course, this may be an artefact of the relatively small numbers of individuals that have been tagged so far – since we know that some British Swifts remain in the Congo Basin overwinter. Perhaps only a proportion of the birds range more widely. The tags also revealed some surprising information about the journey north in spring, which is something for the next chapter.

We talk about the Swift as being the most aerial of our birds, and there is a long-standing conjecture about just how long an individual may remain on the wing without landing. Swifts do not normally breed in their first year, and some individuals may not breed until they reach four years of age, which raises the question about whether or not these non-breeding birds touch down between fledging from their nest and occupying a site of their own. The available evidence used to suggest that young birds were sometimes forced down by periods of bad weather, occasionally roosting on buildings or in trees, but it wasn't until Anders Hedenström and colleagues from Lund University fitted a small number of Swedish Swifts with accelerometers – that enable researchers to record a bird's activity – that we got a more complete picture for adult birds.

The accelerometers revealed that while some individuals never landed during the 10 months of the non-breeding season, most individuals showed very occasional periods of flight inactivity but were otherwise airborne for more than 99% of the time. This work also provided evidence to support the assertion that individual Swifts ascend to altitudes of up to 2,500 m around dusk and dawn, a behaviour that might be linked to navigation but whose origins remain obscure. This behaviour, thought to be a feature of the summer months, was revealed by the accelerometers to occur throughout the year. Some particularly interesting questions remain unanswered; for example, when do Swifts sleep, and for how long; and are their costs of remaining on the wing for such extended periods of time?

Wintering sites and site fidelity

Like the Swift, the Nightjar is a species for which we have, until quite recently, lacked any real knowledge of its wintering areas within Africa. The key books covering African birds all suggest a wintering range which extends from the eastern coast and Kenya down to South Africa, with some also present in West Africa. The results now emerging from various tracking studies, including two involving birds from the UK, describe a somewhat different picture. Nightjars from France, Belgium and the UK have been found to converge on a single wintering area within the southern half of the Democratic Republic of Congo. Most of these birds remain in this area throughout the winter – a period averaging 113 days – and information from three individuals fitted with GPS-tags, suggests that they settle on a winter home range and stay here from November through into February, probably using a favoured roost site each night. The habitats being used by our wintering Nightjars include savannah and scrub-forest; as well as using these habitats for feeding they also take the opportunity to moult their feathers while they are here.

Interestingly, one of the birds from the western European study made an additional migratory movement in late December, the bird relocating to a new site in Namibia. Some of the birds from a Swedish study, whose broader wintering area appears to be located further south than that of the UK birds, also wintered in Namibia. A few individuals also made additional movements during the winter, suggesting some flexibility in wintering strategy and reminiscent of what most of our Swifts do.

Wintering migrants may return to the same sites in consecutive years but there is very little information on the extent to which this occurs. Data from several of the Cuckoos tagged by the BTO indicates a degree of flexibility, with individual birds showing differences in routes and wintering areas between years. These movements appear to be influenced by local conditions, with birds responding to weather conditions (and presumably food availability) by moving elsewhere if necessary. This flexibility in response is particularly evident during the spring migration, when our Cuckoos move north-west into West Africa before their return to the UK (see the next chapter for more on this).

That migrants may winter in different areas in different years is demonstrated by work on Redstarts. Two Redstarts, fitted with geolocators at a breeding site in Denmark, provided migration tracks over two years, with these indicating that the birds were not site faithful between years. Again, the extent to which sites are used across years may be influenced by the predictability of the feeding conditions. A site that sits within a stable environment, say with regular and predictable rains, is likely to have predictable feeding conditions, while one in an arid area with unpredictable rains will be less stable. We know that some species do move around a great deal, following the feeding opportunities; something demonstrated for Montagu's Harrier and with Lesser Kestrel.

It is also evident that particular sites may be used by a succession of birds over a longer period. A study of the Sedge and Reed Warblers wintering site in northern Nigeria has revealed that the Sedge Warblers arrive first, typically from September and into October, and that the Reed Warblers

Esther Tyson
Wheatear
Oils

Esther Tyson
Djoudj
Oils

Esther Tyson
Senegal, West Africa
Oils

arrive later, in November. Regular mist-netting at the site throughout the year, revealed evidence of Sedge Warblers moving through the site, with numbers noticeably higher during the autumn and spring. The pattern for Reed Warblers was different, with numbers steadily increasing from November through to February, after which they began to fall again, ahead of all departures being completed by May. An interesting finding from the regular trapping was that while individual Sedge Warblers were recaptured throughout the winter period, at a similar level to recaptures of the Lesser Swamp Warblers and African Reed Warblers using the site and suggesting they were resident, very few Reed Warblers were recaptured. This might suggest either that the Reed Warblers are highly mobile within the site but move away from the vicinity of the nets or, more likely, they only stay at the site for a short period of time before moving on elsewhere.

Ospreys and wintering waterbirds

Of course it is not just songbirds that make a journey to Africa; joining them are migratory birds of prey, some seabirds, wildfowl and species like Corncrake, Quail, White Stork and Purple Heron. UK Ospreys have been followed to Africa, where they appear to be remarkably faithful to their wintering sites. There is a clear preference for coastal sites in West Africa but Ospreys are found on most waterbodies across the region, including fresh, brackish and salt water sites. Those favouring the coastal zone spend a lot of time loafing around, with just 30 minutes hunting required, on average, to meet their energy needs for the day. Some Ospreys remain in West Africa throughout the year, most of which are young birds in their first or second year. Ospreys typically breed for the first time in their third year, so remaining in Africa for a year or more may be sensible option.

Another familiar raptor in this part of Africa during the winter months is the Marsh Harrier but, since the tendency to migrate decreases as you move from north to south and from east to west across the harrier's breeding range, the individuals wintering in Africa are unlikely to be from our breeding population. Also present are Montagu's Harriers, the European component of which appears to winter within a narrow band of the Sahel within West Africa. As has been revealed by studies of prey remains found within the pellets deposited by these birds at favoured roost sites, large invertebrates, such as grasshoppers and locusts, dominate the diet of these wintering harriers; it is highly likely that the harriers respond to the availability of these prey species by having something of a dynamic distribution during the winter months.

Vast numbers of Garganey and Pintail winter in Africa, occupying wintering grounds that stretch from Senegal in the west, through Sudan and, in the case of Garganey, across into East Africa, with birds found as far south as Uganda and Kenya. One of the major sites for Garganey is the Parc National des Oiseaux du Djoudj in Senegal, where significant numbers of individuals gather to form huge daytime roosts. Roosts may be vacated if there is disturbance from bird-catchers.

The numbers of Garganey taken by the bird-catchers are thought to be somewhere in excess of 10,000 individuals annually. This might seem a lot but it is dwarfed by the numbers shot in southern Europe during migration, which could approach just under 500,000 individuals. The location of feeding sites is also influenced by disturbance, and by the availability of favoured food. Grass seeds, which are the preferred food from October onwards, are replaced by the seeds of sedges and water lilies once supplies have been depleted. Late into the winter both wild and cultivated rice may be targeted by the birds.

Duck catches tend to be higher in dry years, when many small waterbodies dry up and the birds are forced to congregate at a few, well-known sites. Since the dry conditions can also impact the birds through a reduction in food availability, it is difficult to separate out the factors operating on their populations and, ultimately, determining the numbers that survive the winter. The long-term impacts of drought and hunting have also been shaped by changing land use within these areas. Both the abstraction of water for irrigation and the creation of new dams have reduced the amount of natural flooding across the large deltas, such as on the Inner Niger Delta, further concentrating the wintering waterfowl and waders on a smaller number of sites.

The changes taking place on the deltas and across their associated floodplains might also be problematic for wintering Ospreys, many of which appear to be young birds. These floodplains are of minor importance as wintering areas for Ospreys, with many more individuals wintering along the Atlantic coast or at other sites. However, ring-recovery information for those that do choose to winter on the deltas suggests high levels of mortality, linked directly to hunting or accidental capture. One study revealed that a third of the Osprey ring-recoveries reported from the Inner Niger Delta were of individuals accidentally caught when taking a hooked fish; the remaining two thirds were mostly shot or trapped.

Increased exploitation of local fish stocks has seen the disappearance of larger fish from many waterbodies and a decline in fish populations more widely across the region, something that may be increasing competition between the Ospreys and local fishermen. Fortunately, the population trend for European Osprey populations remains favourable, but it is important to keep monitoring the levels of mortality associated with fishing activity in West Africa over the coming years. Information on other potential mortality causes, such as collision with wind turbines, may also be needed.

Robert Greenhalf
Cattle and egrets
Pencil and watercolour

Robert Greenhalf
Grand Lac, Djoudj
Pencil and watercolour

Djoudj - Grande Lac 22.1.2014

Turtle Doves

The loss of the Turtle Dove from much of the UK countryside has been one of the most dramatic changes evident from the series of BTO-led atlas projects, documenting the changing abundance and distribution of Britain and Ireland's breeding birds. The breeding range has contracted back to southern and eastern England, following the complete disappearance from former sites located further north and west. Accompanying this range contraction has been a rapid decline in the breeding population, falling by 97% between 1967 and 2014 according to data from the BTO's core monitoring programmes. This is a species where, potentially, changing pressures on both the breeding and wintering grounds, coupled with continued hunting pressure along the migration routes, are behind the collapse in breeding numbers.

Turtle Dove arrivals in Senegal can begin as early as late July, with new arrivals continuing through into early September. Although significant numbers have remained in Senegal to overwinter in some years – notably when an abundance of rainfall transforms the normally dry Ferlo region of northern Senegal – most move on to winter south or south-east of Senegal, reaching Guinea and Cameroon. Favoured wintering areas combine good feeding opportunities with access to drinking water and groups of trees or small woodlots, which provide cover for roosting and loafing. The initial arrival in Senegal sees the birds visit rice fields, where they feed on grass seeds or scavenge the spilt grains from harvested rice.

It is not until later in the winter that Senegal is again used by significant numbers of wintering doves, as they begin to drift north from February onwards. Some 40 or so years ago many thousands of individuals gathered at favoured sites within the Senegal Delta. A roost near Richard Toll – an area visited by the Flight Lines team during their 2014 trip – reportedly held at least 450,000 Turtle Doves on 13 March 1973, but numbers on this scale are now a thing of the past.

Northern Senegal has traditionally been important for Turtles Doves because of the mix of harvested rice fields, with spilt grain, and rain-fed pools where the birds could drink. This late into the winter the doves will be fuelling for migration and completing their annual moult. Although Turtle Dove numbers using the area have been in decline since the 1970s, there has been an increase in the area under rice cultivation. This cultivation is better managed today than it used to be, with controlled irrigation leading to the loss of natural floodplain vegetation including wild rice and *Acacia* – the former used by the doves for food and the latter for roost sites.

Mali's Inner Niger Delta, the Sahel zone within Burkina Faso, and parts of Cameroon and Nigeria provide important wintering areas for the Turtle Doves breeding in western Europe, although again the numbers here are much reduced compared to what they once were. Land use change and periods of drought have reduced feeding opportunities and, coupled with the removal of the woodlots and scattered *Acacia* scrub used for roosting, the birds have become more concentrated in those areas that still remain suitable. Here they face competition from many other species of dove and pigeon, which also feed on seed, require water and seek suitable roost sites.

In some years, when high rainfall has delivered a superabundance of favoured seeds – such as those of *Panicum*, *Sorghum* and rice (the latter two both being cultivated) – competition is much reduced. However, in dry years the increased levels of competition force the doves to become more specialised in the seeds taken, with European Turtle Doves moving from a diet dominated by *Panicum* to one dominated by *Oryza*. Most of the other dove species also shift their diet away from *Panicum* – African Mourning Dove shifts to *Tribulus*, Vinaceous Dove switches to *Zornia* and *Alysicarpus*, and Laughing Dove shifts to *Gisekia* and *Tribulus* – leaving the Namaqua Dove to feed on *Panicum* and the rhizomes of *Fimbristylis*.

Taking artists to Africa

In January 2014, four SWLA artists – Robert Greenhalf, Bruce Pearson, Greg Poole and Esther Tyson – travelled to West Africa with Phil Atkinson, the BTO's Head of International Research. The purpose of the trip was to visit and document some of the sites used by migrant birds wintering in Senegal, with Phil sharing his knowledge of the birds, the wintering areas and the conservation stories relating to them. For the four artists this was an opportunity to discover the context to what they were seeing and sketching; why did the landscape look the way that it did? What were the birds doing and how were the changes in land use influencing their populations?

Of course the trip was not just about the birds, it was also about the local communities alongside which many of our summer migrants spent the winter. These communities are aware of the arrival of the wintering migrants and, as we have just seen, often view them as a seasonal resource to be exploited, much like the wildfowlers who take wintering waterfowl here in the UK, though with the key difference that the birds are economically more important to African communities than they are to the 'sports-hunters' operating here in Europe.

The Flight Lines team spent two weeks in the northern half of Senegal, arriving in Dakar and then moving quickly north to St. Louis on the coast, from where they were able to spend several days at the Langue du Barbarie reserve. This reserve is dominated by tidal flats and mangroves, attracting a good selection of the migrant waders that winter in West Africa, including Turnstone, Ringed Plover, Wood Sandpiper and Whimbrel. The reserve provided a good introduction to some of the species wintering in Senegal.

Robert Greenhalf
Cormorants and waders
Collagraph

Robert Greenhalf
Whimbrels and godwits
Monoprint

Robert Greenhalf
Warblers and heron
Woodcut

Bruce Pearson
Djoudj landscape
Watercolour/mixed

Bruce Pearson
Sahel
Drypoint/carborundum

Bruce Pearson
Sahel landscape
Graphite

From here the team headed inland to the Parc National des Oiseaux du Djoudj, a World Heritage Site located on the south bank of the Senegal River within the Sahel. Arriving in the dark, the artists were greeted by the calls of several thousand whistling duck – the park holds both White-faced and Fulvous Whistling Duck, the birds using a series of pools close to the entrance track. Djoudj covers some 16,000 hectares and is dominated by wetland habitats, attracting significant numbers of wintering waterbirds including Garganey, Shoveler, Pintail, Ruff and Black-tailed Godwit. Part of the Senegal River Delta, the area holds onto seasonal freshwater for a longer period than the surrounding landscape, making it of particular importance to the wide range of Palearctic migrants that winter or stopover here.

The migrant birds leaving Europe in August and September arrive in the Sahel at the perfect time, when it is wet, green, lush and full of food. As the year progresses so the area dries out and the vegetation dies back. Visiting in mid-winter, the artists found a landscape that retained many temporary waterbodies and was still fairly green. This meant that the team had the opportunity to see and document some of the huge flocks of wintering duck, often in the company of African species like Greater Flamingo, African Spoonbill and Jacana.

Djoudj is a remarkable place, supporting phenomenal numbers of migrants. Chiffchaff are the most ubiquitous in the dry areas but there is a supporting cast of Subalpine, Orphean and Western Olivaceous Warblers. Small numbers of Turtle Doves occur in the grassier areas, while Marsh, Pallid and Montagu's Harriers quarter the scrub and reedbeds. Perhaps the most impressive sights are the roosts – hundreds of thousands, if not millions, of Sand Martins winter here and roost in the reedbeds, while Yellow Wagtails gather on the drier areas before moving into the reedbeds to roost.

After a few days at Djoudj, the team had planned to push east to some of the drier Sahelian landscapes. In the event they found some opportunities just south of the old colonial town of Richard Toll. Away from the undulating landscape of the Senegal River Delta, with its shallow waterbodies and green vegetation, the team encountered dry landscapes, more open and with evidence of the impacts of livestock grazing. The contrast from Djoudj was marked and it seemed strange to see small flocks of Sand Martins feeding over what was essentially semi-desert. Plants such as *Balanaeties*, *Euphorbia* and *Salvadora* dominated the sparse vegetation and small flocks of sandgrouse completed the desert scene.

Nomadic pastoralism is the order of the day in these landscapes and the area was littered by the past presence of large numbers of animals. The area was liberally littered with cow dung, which in turn was spattered with Wheatear droppings. It seemed that in this flat landscape, every little bit of height was an advantage and the area held one of the highest densities of

Photographs
Flight Lines trip to Senegal, West Africa

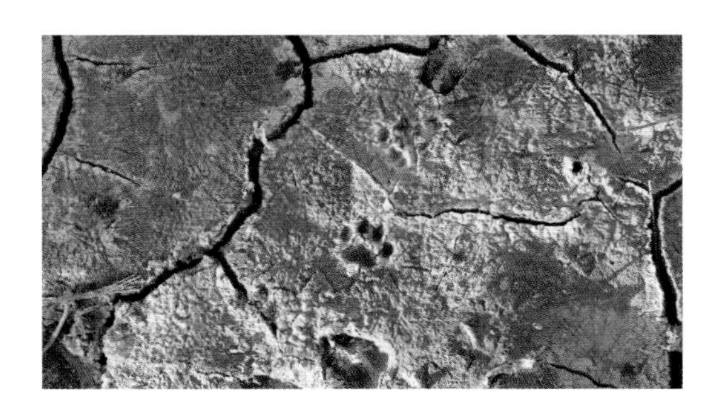

DIARAN

Wheatears that Phil has witnessed in Africa. There was constant activity and 'chakking' as Wheatears flew down to grab insects and scrap with each other at the edge of their territories. Working here was very pleasant but hard and the artists hunkered down to spend some very long days in the sun, finding and documenting the warblers in the bushes. On one occasion a small herd of goats passed through, Yellow Wagtails in their wake. Documenting these landscapes, the livestock and the communities who make a living here, was as an important part of the project as documenting the Wheatears, wagtails and hirundines found to be using the area.

The final part of the trip saw the team relocate to Palmarin, south of Dakar in order to get out of the Sahel and into the Guinea savannah. Palmarin, near the Sine Saloum Delta, is located on a spit of land, with the Atlantic Ocean on one side and lagoons on the other. The artists stayed at a camp located towards the end of the spit, next to a fishing port and from here were able to observe Storm Petrels feeding close in-shore. Away from the port and in the savannah landscapes dominated by scrub and baobabs, the artists and Phil had to work hard to document the wintering migrants. Whitethroat, Subalpine Warbler and Redstart were typical of the migrants here, but the area was also important for birds of prey and it was sometimes possible to see several species in the air together, including Montagu's Harrier and Black-shouldered Kite.

The trip to Senegal, and indeed other components of the BTO/SWLA Flight Lines project, was made possible because of the generous legacy left to the BTO by Penny Hollow, and the kindness of her executors. Penny, a long-standing BTO member, was a regular at SWLA exhibitions, a great supporter and a lay member of the society. The Flight Lines project brought together two of her key loves – birds and art – in a way that we hope has helped to raise the profile of our African migrants. While science can provide the all important evidence upon which conservation decisions and policy can be made and tested, it is our emotional attachment to wildlife that will ultimately drive forward conservation action. Partnering art and science has enabled us to tell the stories of migrant birds in new and engaging ways.

Greg Poole
Nr Richard Toll
Montype

Greg Poole
Coast at Palmarin
Pen

Esther Tyson
Coast at Palmarin
Oil

Velbon

Personal Narrative

The warblers were skulking, but because they moved more slowly they weren't too difficult to watch. Chiffchaffs that would have been quickly flicking around the willows in spring in the UK, over here were much slower... leaner looking.

Phil told us that Whitethroats might have just one *Acacia* bush as their winter home... that would be their territory and they might even return to that same bush in successive years. So you had the sense of the European population of Whitethroats spread out, one to a bush across this belt of Sahel which crosses the continent.

On the plain are three stand-out charismatic species, the Chestnut-bellied Sandgrouse and the two species of courser. Variants on sandy coloration; from the orange sand as freshly dug by ants to the bleached straw of the grass and the umber dung. Raised patches of ground make very low conical mounds blown clean to plaster, the same colour as the breast of the sandgrouse. Around the bird's scapular the spotting is dung coloured; the spots themselves fine spun gold. It is as if I am seeing through the bird to the soil below.

A constant stream of Sand Martins and then waves of Yellow Wagtails pour west into the orange sky; the dry ground gives off a warm glow. The silhouettes of *Acacia*, their leaves folded changing their character... filigree'd, closing shop to the intense sun. Crowned Cranes calling loudly...

Greg Poole
BTO/SWLA Flight Lines trip to Senegal

The return north

Movements within Africa highlight that some species push further south and east as the winter progresses. These birds will start their return north while species wintering further north in Africa are still some way off beginning their spring migrations. The return of our Swifts to Central Africa is one of the first indications that spring is on its way, albeit from several thousand miles away. What happens next is in part determined by rainfall.

There is variation in when birds begin their spring migration, both within and between species wintering in the same area. Individual birds may show consistency in their departure dates from one year to the next, such that some are always amongst the first to leave and others the last. Such differences might be linked to an individual's ability to fatten up, while others might be linked to its age or sex. The location of the breeding grounds may also shape departure dates; in general, for northern hemisphere breeders, populations occupying the southernmost breeding sites will depart first, while those that breed the furthest north depart last. This is evident, for example, across the various races of Yellow Wagtail wintering within Africa, which appear to be distributed latitudinally by race. Individuals of the southern race 'Black-headed' Wagtail are the first to depart, followed by 'Blue-headed', then our race and finally 'Grey-headed'.

Fattening up

Just as for the autumn journey south, the spring migration requires individual birds to lay down the fat reserves required for the first leg of their journey. This may see individuals move from their wintering location to another area, perhaps where drought-breaking rains have led to a flush of invertebrate food. Again, in a similar manner to that seen in autumn, some normally insectivorous birds may switch to fruit, which is energetically rich and quick to convert into fuel for migration. Redstarts and Whitethroats are two species for which fleshy fruit appears to be of particular importance.

For the Garganey overwintering in Senegal or on the Inner Niger Delta, fattening for migration means finding suitable plant material. The grass seeds that were a staple during the early part of the winter will have been depleted, forcing the birds to forage for water lily seeds and cultivated rice. Some indication of the fuel reserves that these ducks are able to lay down ahead of their migration comes from examination of individuals on sale in West Africa's local markets. A small-scale study of the weights of male and female Garganey, on sale during late winter, suggests that females might increase their body weight by 22% between mid-February and mid-March, while males might increase theirs by 29%. In a normal year, with favourable conditions on the Sahelian wintering grounds, the body weights attained by the Garganey just ahead of departure would be sufficient to see them complete a single direct flight to their breeding areas.

Nightjars

For our Nightjars the spring migration begins in late February with a rapid crossing of the rainforest belt. This belt of rainforest is very different to the open habitats that these birds favour in both their breeding and wintering areas, suggesting that it is as much of an ecological barrier as the Mediterranean or the Sahara. Once the birds have crossed the forest they appear to make a brief two-week stopover in Nigeria or Cameroon, an area that they are also likely to have visited during their autumn migration. Departure from this stopover sees their heading switch from north or north-west to west, taking the Nightjars to sites in Guinea and the Ivory Coast where they will make a more prolonged refuelling stop, averaging three weeks. This will be the stopover that fuels the crossing of the Sahara. The desert crossing must take its toll, because the Nightjars stop again in Morocco before entering Europe via Gibraltar or, in the case of at least one tracked individual, via Corsica and mainland France.

Swedish Nightjars, again of which a handful of birds have been tracked using geolocators, follow a broadly similar pattern, making a significant stopover before the desert crossing – this time using the Central African Republic – but seemingly crossing both the desert and the Mediterranean over a nine day period. The Swedish birds cross the central or eastern end of the Mediterranean, using sites in Italy, Greece, Tunisia and Algeria, which suggests that the choice of eastern or western route is determined by the location of the breeding area to which the individuals are heading. Birds from western Europe, including Britain, use the western route, while birds from southern Sweden, and presumably from further east, use the eastern one. Information from more tagged birds will be needed to confirm this and, additionally, to determine the extent to which individual Nightjars are consistent in their choice of route from one year to the next.

The Nightjars show a similar pattern to most of our summer migrants, with the spring migration completed more rapidly than that of autumn. It is thought that there is a selection pressure for birds to reach the breeding grounds as early as possible in order to stand the best chance of securing a prime breeding territory and a high quality mate. Another common feature shared with other migrants is the presence of a loop migration, the spring migration route being to the west of the autumn one. It is well known that small birds often adopt a route that isn't the shortest one between the breeding and wintering areas. Making a detour of this type may be a response to food availability or, as we saw in the chapter in autumn migration, weather patterns. In the case of Nightjars breeding in Britain, France and Belgium, the spring migration route is, on average, a third longer than a direct route would be; it is also longer than the autumn route, which is just 12% longer than the direct route. The importance of the West Africa stopover, and the feeding opportunities associated with it, may be one reason why the spring route is that much longer.

Swifts, Cuckoos and the stopover in West Africa

The use of geolocators has also revealed the importance of a spring stopover site in West Africa for our Swifts. That Swifts which wintered in Central Africa should move west, crossing the Gulf of Guinea to make use of the skies above Liberia ahead of a long desert crossing, implies that this small area delivers important feeding opportunities. The spring rains reach this region in mid-April, just ahead of when the Swifts arrive. A flush in new growth, driving a burst of invertebrate abundance, may be particularly important for birds returning north and about to make a significant desert crossing. One of the tagged UK Swifts spent 10 days in Liberia before making the desert crossing, subsequently covering the 5,000 km back to the UK in just five days.

In Swifts, the spring migration route appears to be similar to that used by the individuals during the autumn, with most birds following a western route that follows Africa's Atlantic seaboard and entry/exit to Europe through the western end of the Mediterranean Basin. There is obviously some ecological advantage to using this western route, since it is favoured by a number of different species, even though it may involve a detour of 40–50% over a more direct crossing of the desert. One of the reasons for choosing this route may be the favourable wind conditions that are encountered by the individuals using it. Swifts moving to the Liberian stopover area from their Central African wintering grounds experience a tail wind during this spring period, something also present when the birds make their crossing of the Sahara. Had these birds attempted to cross the Sahara further east then they would have been flying into a head wind.

Although we only have a small amount of data from across multiple migrations for certain birds, there is evidence that individual Swifts are consistent in their behaviour between years, following the same routes and using the same stopover sites and wintering areas. Something of a similar pattern is emerging from the BTO's satellite-tracked Cuckoos. As we have seen, however, not all individuals do the same thing and there is a degree of variation when we look across the wider population, something that may have significant consequences for individuals and the populations to which they belong.

The information emerging from the many tracking studies now looking at migrant birds wintering in Africa suggests that weather patterns in West Africa influence the timing of the spring migration and shape where individuals stop to refuel ahead of crossing the Sahara. We have already touched on how the seasons work in this part of the continent but it is worth reminding ourselves of this as we consider the pattern of movements evident during the early part of the spring migration. Key to the seasonality of the region is the Intra-tropical Convergence Zone (ITCZ), an east-west rain front that moves north and south throughout the year. At its northernmost extent the ITCZ reaches the Sahel, delivering two months of rain during August and September. The rain front then moves south, crossing the equator to deliver rain to southern Africa. It is as the ITCZ moves north again, several months later, that it shapes the conditions that will be encountered by many of the birds about to begin their spring migration.

The satellite-tags used on the Cuckoos tracked by BTO researchers reveal these initial stages of the journey north in fine detail. Cuckoos wintering in the Congo Basin leave their wintering grounds in February, moving north-west to Nigeria and then continuing west to Ghana and Ivory Coast. The Cuckoos arrive in West Africa over several weeks, and it appears that later departing birds move further west than the first birds to depart. This means that while an early bird might initially stopover in Ghana, a later bird may move direct to Ivory Coast. There is also good evidence emerging from the satellite tracking work of onwards movements, suggesting that the birds are tracking the flush of invertebrates that follows the return of the rains and the burst of new vegetation growth.

Our UK Cuckoos spend several weeks in West Africa, presumably fattening up on caterpillars or other invertebrate prey, before making a swift crossing of the Sahara during the first week or two of April to reach the Mediterranean coast, usually on the African side rather than the European. There is then another stopover before the birds move back to the breeding grounds. That several Afro-Palearctic migrants make stopovers in West Africa underlines the importance of this region and of the drought-busting rains that bring new life to this area.

Photographs
Catching Cuckoos
in Yorkshire and Norfolk

170441

Preparing for the desert crossing

While many species may fuel at sites some distance south of the Sahara, others appear to fuel much close to the desert's southern edge. One of the last vegetated areas that some migrating birds will encounter ahead of the desert crossing on their journey north is the Senegal River Delta, an area that has proved popular with birdwatchers and bird ringers. The first Grasshopper Warblers reach Djoudj in December and captures of new birds by ringers operating at the site increase through from the middle of January and on into February. The high body mass of individuals caught during this period, coupled with the very low numbers of individuals caught at Djoudj in March, suggests that Grasshopper Warblers make their crossing of the Sahara Desert much earlier than most of the small migrants using the site. In fact, the available evidence – and it must be remembered that only relatively small numbers of Grasshopper Warblers have been caught and ringed on migration – suggests that many cross the Sahara early in the year and then spend significant time further north within Africa before crossing into Europe. Grasshopper Warblers do not appear to pass through the Straits of Gibraltar until late March, so they could well be using undiscovered sites in Morocco or elsewhere within the north-west of Africa.

The dry season in this part of the Sahel, within which Djoudj and the delta sit, peaks in March and early April. This means that the Grasshopper Warblers arriving in January and February will be facing deteriorating conditions and this may explain why they move on as soon as they can. This suggestion is supported by information gained through the ringing expeditions that have visited the area. These have revealed that Grasshopper Warblers using Djoudj during their northward migration are slow to take on board the fuel loads necessary to make the desert crossing. The rates of body mass gain are far lower than seen in this species during the autumn migration at stopover sites in Portugal, and also much lower than seen in other small passerines refuelling on their spring migration at sites elsewhere within West Africa. Parallel studies in Djoudj and Portugal have revealed that stopover length in Djoudj is nearly twice the length of that seen in Portugal.

Not all migrants appear to make a detour across West Africa in spring. There is evidence, admittedly only from a small number of tagged individuals, that Redstarts may take a more direct route north than that used when heading south in the autumn. All five individuals fitted with geolocators at a breeding site in southern Sweden, made a northwards spring movement from their wintering grounds in Mali and Burkina Faso, rather than moving west to the Atlantic coast to retrace their autumn route. This creates a loop in which the birds are further east on their return journey and reduces the distance to be travelled, perhaps reflecting the pressure to reach the breeding grounds early. As they had done during the autumn,

Richard Johnson
Cuckoo, Wicken
Watercolour

these birds still made two brief stopovers during the course of the journey north, one around the western end of the Mediterranean – either in North Africa or southern Spain, and one in central Europe, south of the breeding grounds.

After the desert

Earlier in the book we saw how most small migrant birds cross the Sahara by flying at night and then resting during the day. This strategy minimises energetic costs and maintains a favourable water balance but, even allowing for this, most migrants still need to stop and refuel in North Africa or southern Europe before pushing on towards their breeding grounds. The question of where individuals choose to stop is likely to depend on the amount of fuel they are carrying after the desert crossing, since this will determine the range possible for any onward movement.

There are vegetated areas directly north of the desert, in places like southern Morocco, but these are likely to be less productive than sites further north on the other side of the Mediterranean, which are less dry and have a greater abundance of insect life. For a spring migrant, the decision is whether to stop early but take on board fuel at a slower rate, because food is harder to come by, or to stop later, where food is more abundant, and be able to lay down fat reserves at a much faster rate. Work in southern Morocco has provided at least some of the answers to this dilemma, by looking at the condition of arriving migrants and determining how much further they could have flown before stopping. The ecologists working on this study have found that some species typically arrive in relatively good condition, with Swallow and Pied Flycatcher two of these, but that other species are in relatively poor condition; these include Redstart, Willow Warbler and Yellow Wagtail. Interestingly, the Wheatears arriving at the site are usually in very poor condition, in terms of fat reserves, but it is known that this species generally carries low fuel reserves on migration because it can stop each day and find food, being an active hunter on open ground.

The flight range estimates calculated from this study reveal that most of the individuals stopping at the site needed a refuelling stopover somewhere in North Africa in order to reach Europe, but fewer than a third of the individuals in most of the species studied actually needed to refuel at the study site itself, suggesting that they could have pushed on a bit further. The good condition of the arriving Pied Flycatchers was further emphasised by the fact that more than half of the individuals encountered would have been able to reach southern Spain without an additional fuelling stop, the only species in which this was the case. The Pied Flycatchers arrive at the site quite late in the season, raising the possibility that they might spend more time at sites to the south of the desert so that they don't have to stop again

John Threlfall
Pied Flycatcher study
Pencil and watercolour

Dafila Scott
Hobby
Pastel

before reaching Europe – a similar strategy has been proposed for Garden Warbler. Choice of stopover sites north of the desert may also be influenced by the habitat preferences of the different species. Other work in Morocco found that those species adapted to drier habitats, such as Subalpine Warbler, were more likely to utilise sites closer to the desert than species adapted to habitats with higher humidities and lusher vegetation.

Looking more broadly across the Mediterranean, and in particular at the standardised ringing sessions operated on many Mediterranean islands and at sites on Europe's southern coast, it is possible to gain a greater insight into the strategies used on the journey north. This work emphasises that most small passerines undertake a direct flight from stopover sites south of the Sahara, crossing both the desert and the Mediterranean in a single hop. Individual birds, migrating mostly at night, may make daytime stops while crossing the desert, but are likely to continue their nocturnal flights into the daylight hours when crossing the sea, something that is evident from the arrival times of birds reaching the more northerly ringing stations. Average body masses of birds arriving at the ringing stations are close to the lean body mass estimates for the species studied, suggesting that individuals are not infrequently at the limit of their flying capacity. This makes stopover sites close to the desert's southern edge all the more important, since these appear to be the only fuelling option for many of the birds moving north.

The extent to which stopover sites in Africa, north of the Sahara, are used by birds on their spring migration is something that requires further study. The apparently conflicting results sometimes seen in the different studies so far conducted might be explained by the nature of the landscapes as you move from west to east across North Africa. Morocco, with the Atlas Mountains, may well have suitable conditions for migrating birds to stop and refuel before an onwards journey across the Mediterranean. However, as you move east conditions may become less favourable and it may be this that influences the decision to continue onwards. It would be useful to examine the fat loads of birds as they leave sites to the south of the desert, since this might provide an indication of likely flight ranges, some of which might be found to differ between individuals of the same species depending on where they are along the east–west gradient.

Predation

One factor not mentioned in detail during the section on autumn migration, but worthy of mention here, is predation. Predators can take a significant toll on migrant birds and, for those species making the journey to and from Africa, it is a suite of five predatory falcons that needs to be considered. Two of these – Eleonora's Falcon and Sooty Falcon – time their breeding season to exploit small passerines on their autumn migration. Three others –

Szabolcs Kókay
Stone-curlew
Watercolour

Peregrine Falcon, Barbary Falcon and Lanner Falcon – breed early in the year to take advantage of small birds on spring passage. Back in the 1970s it was estimated that the global population of c.10,000 Eleonora's Falcons took 1-2 million migrant birds annually.

An additional and perhaps surprising predator of migrant song birds was only recently revealed. The Giant Noctule Bat *Nyctalus lasiopterus*, which has a wingspan of 18 inches, was first suspected of feeding on migrant birds when feather fragments were found in droppings collected in Spain. More recent work has revealed a seasonal switch in the bat's diet, away from insects, which are favoured in summer, to birds which dominate the autumn diet. Interestingly, the spring diet contains a mix of birds and insects, perhaps reflecting that birds are less readily available during the spring migration. The Giant Noctule Bat has a patchy breeding distribution, extending across southern Europe, north-west Africa and into Asia. Quite how the bat manages to catch small birds – Robin and Wood Warbler are among the species confirmed as prey – is unclear, but it seems likely that at least some are caught in flight. For a bat weighing just 35–53g, the capture of a Robin in flight would add an additional 50% to the body weight of the flying bat.

Spring weather

Migrant birds, heading north during early spring, must ensure that they do not arrive on their breeding grounds before feeding conditions are suitable for replenishing fuel reserves expended on the journey or required for breeding. Weather conditions are likely to be worse closer to the breeding sites than they are further south at this time of the year, something that has a greater impact on early migrants than it does those on those that typically arrive later into the year. Bad weather on the journey north can halt spring migration, as individuals are grounded or delayed by rain, strong head-winds and blocking weather systems. In some years such systems can delay arrivals by several days, maybe even longer, subsequently releasing the back-log of birds that has built up, most likely somewhere in southern Europe. These birds can then suddenly arrive on the breeding grounds in large numbers, much to the delight of expectant birdwatchers.

The use of satellite-tags has revealed how individual birds may respond to poor conditions on the journey north; for example, some of the BTO's tagged Cuckoos were seen to make a 'U' turn and retreat south when they encountered poor weather during their spring migration. This is not always an option, however, and birds may get caught out by particularly poor weather, perhaps resulting in substantial mortality if, for example, they run into heavy rain storms. Swallows and House Martins are species where substantial losses have been documented as a consequence of particularly rough weather. Other individuals may become disorientated and end up many hundreds of miles from their intended destination. This is one of the causes of vagrancy and the arrival of birds likely to attract a sizeable crowd of birdwatchers. A feature of spring migration is the arrival in the UK of birds that breed further south in Europe, these individuals effectively overshooting their intended destination.

The ability to keep track with the feeding conditions required on the journey north is obviously related to the speed of spring migration. Species that tend to move north across Europe in a series of short flights – perhaps of 50–200 km at a time – should be able to keep more in step with feeding conditions than species that undertake much longer flights. Such differences might also explain why some migrants show more consistency in their arrival dates, matching better with spring temperatures on the breeding grounds, than others. It is the pattern of arrivals that we will consider in the next chapter.

Toby Smith
Gabon landscape
Photograph

Toby Smith
Activity at the river
Photograph

Toby Smith
Classroom exercise
Photograph

9 Janvier 2016
lecture: u u u u
N n
nie. Elle est punie.
la lune
le jus
une maman
né nè nê
a natte- la lune
elle dîne-

Personal Narrative

Malcolm Green and I felt a mixture of excitement, disbelief and relief as we squinted at the cursor on the GPS screen. After six days of hard travelling; 15 hours of flights, 18 hours by train, 220 km gruelling off-road driving and 8 km on foot, we finally stood in a picturesque valley frequented by two of the BTO's tagged Cuckoos. Cuckoo flight data and our stubborn resolve had led us to a remote part of the Batéké Plateau, in eastern Gabon, close to the Congolese border.

Visually this landscape is the sister of Cumbria or central Wales. Lone trees, serving as ideal perches, stud verdant grass and rolling scrubland fringed by rich gallery forest under a porcelain blue sky. Yet my other senses painted a very different picture. The air is fragrant but arid, the sun fierce and the heat utterly oppressive.

The Cuckoo is one of Britain's best loved and studied migratory birds. We adore its distinctive call and cheeky breeding habits but our empathy and understanding has thus far been restricted to our shores and done little to halt a rapid population decline. The BTO's study empirically proves, that after an epic and perilous journey, our Cuckoos spend the majority of winter here in Central Africa.

Packing a long lens or binoculars and attempting to spot a Cuckoo was a distraction, it felt frivolous and even selfish. Instead I was determined to explore, document and publish the human and geographic narratives that the birds inhabit and share in Gabon. In so doing I hope to bring this little known country closer to home and help focus a future lens of conservation efforts and study towards it.

Toby Smith
Photojournalist.

Arrivals

There is something special about the sight and sound of the first spring migrants, something that hints at the season ahead and provides reassurance that all is right with the world. While these first individuals may appear days or even weeks ahead of the main arrival, they are what we, as birdwatchers, watch for with a sense of expectation. Each is duly noted and the date of its appearance compared with that of previous years. The progression of arrivals runs over many weeks, most likely beginning with Chiffchaff and ending with Spotted Flycatcher. The pattern of arrivals in most birdwatcher's notebooks owes something to chance, to the timing of particular weather events that help or hinder northward migration or to whether or not you have the opportunity to be out birdwatching when a species happens to put in an appearance. It is only when we can look across the records of many hundreds or even thousands of birdwatchers that we can view the underlying patterns and the pulse of migrant birds pouring into Britain.

A succession of arrivals

Taken as a whole, the pattern of arrivals seen across the various different species reveals the underlying influence of food availability during the spring migration period. Some of the earliest species to arrive back at their breeding grounds are the waterfowl, many of which will be moving to sites located much further north than the UK. These birds need to time their migration so that they arrive on their breeding sites after the spring thaw has released their food supplies. Next come those migrants that feed on ground-dwelling insects, then aerial insects – the Swallows and martins – with early individuals often associating with wetland habitats, where these insects first emerge. Later still come the warblers and other species that feed predominantly on the caterpillars and other larvae of leaf-feeding insects, which only appear after buds have burst and leaves expanded.

Species arriving later tend to travel north more quickly, something evident from ring-recoveries and from the cumulative records of birdwatchers operating across a continental scale. These differences in the speed of northward migration can be seen in the time taken for a species to progress from southern Europe to its more northerly breeding grounds, first documented in a series of papers published in the journal British Birds on the eve of the Second World War – and perhaps in need of revisiting. These papers, written by Henry Southern, revealed that the early-arriving Swallow – which typically reached the southern shores of Europe during the second week of February – took 109 days to reach its more northerly breeding grounds. Willow Warbler, which arrived in southern Europe at the start of March, took an average of 88 days, while Redstart (arriving mid-March) took just 61 days. Southern was particularly interested in the relationship between the speed of onward progression and the availability of favoured prey.

Information on the arrival patterns of summer migrants breeding in the UK now comes from BirdTrack (www.birdtrack.net), a BTO-led project that provides facilities for birdwatchers to store and manage their birdwatching records, at the same time enabling these observations to be used to support conservation and research into the movements and distribution of species. BirdTrack is a great example of 'citizen science' and stems from the idea that the observations made by birdwatchers – whether at a nature reserve or in a garden – can provide valuable information. Key to the success of the project has been its ability to communicate the value of birdwatching lists, where observers confirm that they have recorded all of the birds seen or heard during a visit to a particular site. The proportion of lists containing a given species provides a good measure of the frequency of occurrence; it is this information that can be used to chart the spread of migrants as they arrive in the UK – and again as they depart.

An early exploration of the BirdTrack records by the BTO's Stephen Baillie revealed a progression of arrivals similar to that already outlined above; among the aerial insectivores, for example, Sand Martin arrived first, followed by Swallow, House Martin and then Swift. The species examined showed a clear progression across the UK, arriving first in the south-west and last in the north-east. There were also some interesting species-specific patterns. Wheatear showed a double peak in arrivals, the first relating to the arrival of local, UK-breeding individuals and the second, later peak representing the through passage of the larger race, breeding in Greenland. The pattern seen for Wheatear also demonstrates that the arrival of a species, and its onward movement, may not be restricted to a single, short and clearly defined period. Some species show a protracted pattern of arrival, while in others it is more focused. The extent to which arrivals are focused or not appears to be related to the size of the breeding range occupied. Birds that breed within a narrow band of latitude tend to arrive within a small window, while those breeding over a larger area have a much bigger window within which movements take place. As we saw in an earlier chapter – though in a different context – Yellow Wagtail is such a species. Breeding areas tend to be occupied from south to north, with individuals breeding the furthest north arriving later.

Gaining an advantage

We have already touched on the benefits that may be gained by early arrival back on the breeding grounds, which include a greater opportunity to secure a high-quality territory and mate. There is plenty of evidence from published research that, across a range of bird species, the best quality territories on a site are always occupied first, even if the occupants have changed between years. Early arrival provides the opportunity for birds to start breeding earlier and it is interesting to note that these early nesting attempts are usually more productive than those started later in the year. Early arrival might also afford a single-brooded species the opportunity to initiate another nesting attempt should the first one fail during the incubation or early chick period.

Of course, arriving too early can incur considerable costs, with an individual potentially encountering adverse weather or poor feeding conditions. Arriving late can mean a bird failing to align the peak food demands of its chicks with the peak availability of preferred prey. This is referred to as phenological mismatch and is something that we will look at in more detail in the next chapter. Taken together, the competing pressures probably act to squeeze the timing of spring arrival into a narrower window than that seen during the period of autumn departure.

Late arriving species often initiate their breeding attempt fairly soon after arrival, something that is in contrast to what is seen in early arriving species like Chiffchaff. Chiffchaffs reach southern England in the first half of April but do not usually initiate nesting attempts until early May. The Willow Warblers arriving in late April/early May, however, typically have their first eggs within a fortnight, suggesting they are under pressure to get started. Willow Warbler is a single-brooded species, while Chiffchaff is double-brooded.

Arrival date may be influenced by where the bird has spent the winter, by the number and location of stopover sites used on the journey north, and by the weather conditions encountered along the way. Each of these different factors may be the most important for a particular species, or indeed a particular population. Earlier we saw how British and Dutch Pied Flycatchers winter further east in West Africa than those breeding in Scandinavia, with the suggestion that early arrival on the wintering grounds allows British and Dutch birds to occupy better quality sites that also happen to be closer to their breeding areas. More recent work, carried out

Richard Johnson
Garganey, Burwell
Watercolour

by Janne Ouwehand and Christiaan Both, has revealed that, for Dutch Pied Flycatchers at least, variation in arrival dates at the breeding sites is the result of variation in when the birds depart from their wintering quarters and not the result of conditions encountered along the route. The rapid spring migration from West Africa, averaging just two weeks, sees male Pied Fycatchers arrive back on the breeding grounds ahead of the females, who depart slightly later. Information from the small number of UK Pied Flycatchers fitted with geolocators suggests a departure from the wintering grounds in the last week of March and arrival at breeding sites during the second half of April.

This pattern of Pied Flycatcher arrivals dovetails rather nicely with earlier work, which looked at the whole annual cycle and revealed that autumn migration schedules are adjusted according to breeding duties; birds with late broods make their autumn departures later than those birds whose young have already fledged. Taken together, this suggests that individuals may have to adjust their annual strategy because of breeding commitments, but it does also raise the question of what the consequences of a late departure might be. Work in Ivory Coast suggests that in good quality habitats Pied Flycatchers will maintain and defend a winter territory, returning to it in successive years. If a bird holding such a territory in one year gets away from the breeding grounds late the following year, will it still be able to take ownership of that territory?

Change over time

The records of arrivals and departures collected by birdwatchers over a great many years mean that we now have more information on the timing of migration than on any other aspect of this strongly seasonal process. Researchers have used this information to examine the extent to which the timing of migration – most notably spring migration – has changed over time. It is well established that a whole series of conspicuous spring events, from the arrival of migrant birds to the spawning of frogs and the flowering of trees, now occur earlier than they once did, collectively delivering a sense that spring now happens that much earlier in the year. The timing of these biological events – the study of which is known as phenology – is one of the things that first alerted us to the impacts of rising greenhouse gas concentrations and a changing climate.

In response to a changing climate and increasing global temperatures, the arrival (and departure) dates of many migrants have changed. BTO researchers have been able to use BirdTrack observations, together with those collected through the Inland Observation Point survey, which the BTO operated from October 1962 to November 1966, to test this. Both of the surveys used standardised methods to collect their information, allowing data from the studies to be compared and for the pattern of arrivals and departures to be documented. This study was led by Stuart Newson, a research ecologist working across a suite of the BTO's core monitoring schemes to examine changing patterns of distribution and occurrence.

The arrival dates for 11 of the 14 common migrant species examined by Stuart and his colleagues have become significantly earlier, with six species advancing their arrival by more than 10 days since the 1960s. These include the three hirundines (Swallow, Sand Martin and House Martin), together with Redstart, Chiffchaff and Blackcap. The change in spring arrival across the species studied equates to an advance of 0.22 days per year on average, a not insignificant change. In addition to the change noted in arrival dates, four of the species (Blackcap, Chiffchaff, Garden Warbler and Whinchat) were found to depart significantly later. The net result of these advancements and delays is that the length of stay for nine of the 14 species has become significantly longer.

One of the last of our summer migrants to return is the Swift, typically arriving back on the breeding grounds in late April or early May. Like many of our other migrants, analyses of the BirdTrack data suggest that Swifts now arrive earlier than they did just a few decades ago; at 4.7 days this difference is less than that seen in other species and, importantly, other work suggests it might not have advanced at all. Swifts also appear to leave our shores earlier than they once did – which is the opposite from what we are seeing with other migrants – so they could potentially spend less time here in the UK than they used to.

A network of observatories

Another source of information on the arrivals of spring migrants comes from the network of bird observatories located around the coasts of Britain and Ireland. The individual observatories are independent, often run as a trust or small charity and staffed by a mix of volunteers and paid staff. Their work is coordinated through the Bird Observatories Council, formed in 1946 and made up of representatives from each of the 18 accredited observatories, together with staff from the BTO.

A central component of the daily routine at a bird observatory is the collation of the daily census, bringing together information from standardised counts of the birds seen or caught throughout the day. For many of the observatory staff and volunteers it is the BirdTrack system into which the census data are entered, adding to a national data set that can be used by researchers and conservation practitioners. Much of the data from earlier decades has yet to be computerised – a huge task in itself – but more and more records are now being stored electronically, greatly increasing their value for those studying migration.

The daily counts can reveal fine-scale detail within the spring and autumn migration periods, similar to the pattern of Wheatear arrivals mentioned earlier but more subtle because of the species involved. John Marchant and Chris Wernham, for example, have looked at the autumn migration patterns for Willow Warblers passing through Dungeness Bird Observatory from 1960 to 2000. Their study revealed that the autumn passage of Willow Warblers at Dungeness Bird Observatory showed a double or treble peak during August. While the reasons for these different peaks could not be determined, it was thought that they might relate to birds of different age-classes or from different breeding areas. It is this sort of information that can help to tease out the different migration strategies being used by different populations or particular cohorts of individuals. It might, for example, indicate whether the adults and juveniles of a species are doing different things.

It is worth emphasising that bird observatories play another important role in enabling and encouraging volunteers and other visitors to participate in scientific studies of birds, other taxa and the environment. They are a place where interested individuals can see birds at close quarters and engage with the work being done by ringers and other BTO volunteers.

Harnessing enthusiasm

The enthusiasm shown for birds and for birdwatching has enabled organisations like the BTO to carry out important work, monitoring the changing fortunes of bird populations and establishing why their numbers change. This type of work, which is based around surveying their populations, monitoring their breeding attempts and revealing their movements and demography (productivity and mortality), relies on volunteers. The BTO/JNCC/RSPB Breeding Bird Survey, for example, which is the main scheme for establishing what is happening to UK bird populations, sees volunteers visit in excess of 3,500 survey squares each year. Attaining these levels of coverage by using just paid professionals would be impossible.

BTO volunteers participating in the Nest Record Scheme, of which there are 700 individuals, monitor roughly 45,000 breeding attempts each year, aiming to visit each nest several times to secure accurate measures of first egg date (a standard measure used to look at the timing of breeding), clutch size, brood size and outcome. Simply finding the nests of some species can involve a significant amount of effort, the volunteers using all of their skills to pinpoint the site. In some species this can involve watching the behaviour of the adult birds, often from some distance, and using certain behavioural clues to establish where the nest is located. In other species, such as those using nest boxes, it is more straightforward. Nest recording provides

Matt Underwood
House Martins
Collagraph

Harriet Mead
Scissor Stone-curlew
Welded found objects

Brin Edwards
Stone-curlews with hare
Oil on canvas

Robert Greenhalf
Wheatear and Swifts
Woodcut

information that can be used to establish whether changes in productivity are behind population declines revealed by the Breeding Bird Survey and other surveys.

An incredible effort is invested by the 2,600 trained and licensed bird ringers who participate in the Ringing Scheme. Ringing birds is essential if we are to learn about where and when they move, and about how long they live. We have already seen examples throughout this book where the use of bird ringing has made a significant difference to our understanding of migration, of the routes used and of the challenges that migrating birds face. Placing a lightweight, uniquely numbered, metal ring on a bird's leg is a reliable and harmless method for identifying birds as individuals. It is by being able to recognise a bird as an individual that we can understand the degree to which survival influences population trends.

Although we have been ringing birds in Britain and Ireland for over 100 years, as this book reveals, we are still discovering new facts about migration routes and wintering areas. Today, however, the main focus of the Ringing Scheme is the monitoring of bird populations and the study of how many birds leaving the nest go on to survive and become adults. It also tells us how many adults survive the stresses of breeding, migration and severe weather. Alongside other aspects of birds biology, changes in survival rates help us to understand the causes of population declines.

For many BTO volunteers the arrival of spring signals another field season and another year of valuable contribution to the surveys and schemes underpinning much of the conservation action directed towards our wild bird populations. Our focus in this book has been on Afro-Palearctic migrants, but it is important to recognise that BTO volunteers collect a wealth of information across all of the UK's bird species, from monthly surveys of waders and wildfowl, through to weekly counts of garden birds and the reporting of wildlife disease.

opticron

Personal Narrative

The phrase 'a bird's eye view' may conjure up notions of an aerial perspective but for those of us obsessed with Reed Warblers, the reality is quite different. From March to August, I spend my wetsuit-clad days wading through the *Phragmites* fringes of my local gravel pit. Some might find pushing through endless reeds claustrophobic, such is the density of the vegetation, but for me the thrill of being in the thick of it, having nature almost literally in your face, day after day, never diminishes.

The sense of season nest recording offers is, in my opinion, unsurpassed. At the outset, I'm surrounded only by dead stems, easily locating the first Coot and grebe nests. As April begins, so the first vivid green reed spears are piercing the surface, and by the start of May there is often enough structure to support the nests of the first Reed Warblers, tightly tied to their transient host. By June the stems extend well above head height and the air is thick with insects, a constantly shifting mix of the beautiful and the biting that sustains many of the nestlings I study. The next two months pass rapidly in an intense flurry of activity for parent bird and researcher alike, and at times in July it can feel that the cacophonous mass of fledgling warblers bouncing around the reeds outnumbers their invertebrate prey. The last chicks typically leave the nest in mid-August and the site in late September, a good month after their parents and a few weeks before I migrate back to the terrestrial world.

Dave Leech
BTO Head of Ringing & Nest Recording

Breeding grounds

Pied Flycatchers and Redstarts

The Pied Flycatchers whose journeys we have explored throughout the course of this book have been well-studied on their breeding grounds. One of the main reasons for this is the willingness of the species to make use of nestboxes, something that has afforded ringers, nest recorders and university academics the opportunity to study their breeding ecology and return rates. It is only recently, with the emergence of new tracking technologies, that we have been able to piece together information on their ecology and distribution outside of the breeding season. There is much still to learn and nestbox studies here in Britain and Ireland will continue to be an important component of this work. While tracking devices can provide us with much more detail on the movements of individual birds than is attainable from ringing, structured ringing programmes provide the all-important information on survival rates.

For Pied Flycatcher, some of the UK effort is coordinated through PiedFly.net, set up by Malcolm Burgess. PiedFly.net is a non-profit organisation, coordinating volunteer participation in the monitoring of Pied Flycatchers and other hole-nesting woodland birds. The network coordinates the monitoring of nestbox schemes across the south-west of England. Many of the individual schemes linked through PiedFly.net have been operating for some time; previously, only a small number of the schemes contributed data to national monitoring programs, but since 2011 the network has brought all this information together to share with national schemes and the wider scientific community. The species also features prominently in the BTO's ringing-based Retrapping Adults for Survival project, which uses information from 23 different schemes to generate information on long-term trends in Pied Flycatcher survival rates. For migrant birds, a sudden change in survival rates can indicate problems away from the breeding grounds, either on migration or on the wintering areas.

The woodland sites used by breeding Pied Flycatchers, which are to be found in the western half of Britain, are also home to breeding Redstarts – which also occupy the nestboxes – and Wood Warblers – which don't. Both of these species winter in Africa. Many of the woodland sites used by these species are damp, with mature Oak and Birch covered in moss and lichen delivering a sense of great age. For the ringers fortunate enough to work them, they can be a magical place, although some of the woods are easier to work than others. Steep ground, wet moss-covered rocks and clouds of midges are just some of the challenges faced by the volunteers who monitor the nestbox schemes directed at these summer migrants.

The Pied Flycatcher is one of the 10 most abundant small migrants using the Afro-Palearctic flyway, with a breeding range that extends right across Europe. This fact, coupled with its willingness to use nestboxes, makes it an ideal study species for academics and other researchers seeking to address questions about the timing of migration and the influences of climate and changes in land use. Being able to bring together detailed information on breeding ecology for individual birds – adult Pied Flycatchers can be safely trapped at the nestbox – with information on their migration routes, wintering grounds and the timing of their movements, means that we have an opportunity to unravel the complexities of being a migrant bird in a changing world.

Phenological mismatch

The Pied Flycatcher has been particularly useful as a study species for those researchers examining phenological mismatch. This occurs where key events in the life of a species no longer match with key events in another species on which they depend. An example of this is the timing of reproduction in insectivorous birds like tits and Pied Flycatchers, which seek to match the period of peak food demand for their chicks with the peak abundance of their caterpillar prey. Climate change has seen leaf burst in many trees advance and occur earlier in the year than it did just a few decades ago. Moth populations, which rely on the young leaves for food, have responded to this and have largely been able to keep up with the changing availability of their food. Moths can do this because they have a short generational time, allowing a rapid evolutionary response, but the birds that rely on the caterpillars cannot respond as quickly, meaning that they might no longer be able to match the timing of peak food demand for their chicks with the peak availability of caterpillars.

There has been some debate around the extent to which phenological mismatch is behind some of the recent declines seen in migrant birds. There is good evidence from elsewhere in Europe that a number of the species feeding on woodland caterpillars – including both migrants like Pied

Flycatcher and residents like Great Tit – are suffering from reduced breeding success because they are now nesting later than the peak availability of their favoured caterpillar prey. This mismatch between food demand and prey availability is thought to have brought about recent declines in the populations of Pied Flycatchers breeding in Dutch woodlands.

Mismatch might be more of a problem for migrant species because they are less able to advance the timing of their breeding season than resident species, with constraints on spring arrival times limiting opportunities for change in the timing of breeding. At large spatial scales, such as those experienced by birds wintering in Africa but breeding in the UK, climate change impacts may differ substantially between breeding and wintering areas, quite possibly placing further stress on migrant populations already facing the challenge of habitat change. In a study looking at breeding birds in the Netherlands, researchers found that long distance migrants which bred in the most seasonal habitats – i.e. those where climate change effects might be felt most strongly – and which arrived on the breeding grounds latest, showed the most negative population trends; Pied Flycatcher was one such species. Within the UK we have also seen a decline in Pied Flycatcher populations; interestingly; over the same period UK Great Tit populations have increased, which suggests that for this resident species any reduction in productivity as a result of mismatch is more than compensated for by other factors, such as improved overwinter survival.

A change in the weather

Another species in which researchers have sought to reveal the potential impacts of phenological mismatch is the Swallow. Using data on Swallow breeding ecology from the BTO's Nest Record Scheme and on aerial insect populations from the Rothamsted Insect Survey, operated by Rothamsted Research, Blaise Martay and colleagues have looked for evidence of phenological mismatch over a 30-year period. The breeding data reveal that Swallows advanced their breeding season by 0.285 days/year between 1972 and 2002; there's also been a change in the abundance and seasonality of aerial insect populations over this period. The study showed that food availability affected Swallow breeding success but concluded that phenological mismatch was unlikely to have had a large influence on Swallow populations. It is thought that species like Swallow may be at less risk of mismatch than species feeding within woodland on caterpillars because their prey are not so strongly seasonal in their occurrence.

The results of the work on Swallows also highlights the potential impacts within a breeding season of a run of poor weather. Since Swallow productivity is linked to prey availability, it follows that if poor weather reduces the numbers of insects flying, there will be fewer prey available to a hunting Swallow. Swallows may attempt to counter poor feeding conditions by shifting their feeding site, perhaps foraging lower over the ground or moving to more sheltered spots where flying insects are still active.

Swifts may be able to respond to periods of bad weather during the breeding season. Although most of the Swifts breeding in our towns and cities feed close to the colony, allowing them to make up to 8–10 visits to the nest daily, it is thought that they may make long distance movements in search of food if the local weather conditions are unfavourable. Various authors have suggested that Swifts skirt around approaching depressions, flying into the wind in order to reach better weather conditions elsewhere, perhaps even crossing the Channel to feed. This, however, has yet to be documented with tagged birds.

Although it appears to be the weather on the wintering grounds that has a significant impact on the survival of adult birds like Whitethroat, Sand Martin and Sedge Warbler, a few studies have found breeding season weather to influence apparent survival rates the following year. Edward Cowley's long-term data set of Sand Martins breeding at sites in Nottinghamshire, stimulated by the BTO Sand Martin Enquiry and analysed in collaboration with Gavin Siriwardena, found that breeding season rainfall had a greater impact on overwinter survival than that resulting from a lack of rainfall on the West African wintering grounds themselves. As with Swallow, summer rainfall probably also impacts the breeding success of this species by reducing the availability of the aerial insects on which these birds feed.

The forest at night

Not all of our summer migrants are as visible as Swifts and Swallows. Some have a more restricted distribution, use habitats that are visited less often or are active at times of day when we are not. One of these is the Nightjar, an otherworldly bird, with its alien call, whiskered face and soft frog-like gape. It is nocturnal, extremely well camouflaged and a summer visitor about which, until recently, we knew surprisingly little. Fortunately, our knowledge of these summer visitors is changing, thanks to the efforts of Ian Henderson and Greg Conway, two BTO research ecologists whose evenings and weekends are given over to finding and studying Nightjars in Thetford Forest, a vast lowland plantation that straddles the Norfolk/Suffolk border. By also working with volunteers at other sites, Ian and Greg are learning many new things about these birds, their breeding ecology and migration patterns. The Nightjar project provided an opportunity for SWLA artists to see Nightjars and the work being done on them.

It is at night that Thetford Forest, with its managed blocks of conifers and clearfell, is transformed into something else, as if it almost begins to re-inhabit something of the lost wilderness. The pattern of these commercial

Richard Johnson
Cuckoo study. Burwell
Watercolour

Michael Warren
Sand Martin story
Watercolour

3 – Langford Lowfields – Nottinghamshire – May 2015.
The Sand Martins abandon the nesting bank – the three previous years since creation of bank by RSPB had seen 100+ pairs nest –

2 – Langford Lowfields – Nottinghamshire – April 2015
There is some activity at the nesting bank but cool wet conditions persist – About 30 attempts at excavating holes – but none completed –

Esther Tyson
Sand Martins
Screenprint

plantations is such that areas of clearfell are separated by blocks of regrowth of varying ages, culminating in the mature stands that shorten horizons with their deep shadow. It is to one of these blocks that we have brought sculptor Harriet Mead and painter and print-maker Esther Tyson; tonight we hope to guide them to a sitting female Nightjar so they can document her, and her forest landscape, through their artwork. Ian and Greg have identified this female as being suitable to carry one of their tiny tracking devices for a few nights. These tags can pinpoint a bird's position to within a few metres, taking a location every few minutes and revealing how the bird uses the forest and the surrounding landscape. The bird will be recaptured in a few days, the tag removed and the data downloaded.

Greg guides us in towards the first bird, whose nest was found earlier in the week during a daytime survey. The location of the nest has been marked by some carefully placed sticks, positioned a few metres away. A passing walker would miss their significance, but to Greg they mark a safe route in. We halt, three rows of trees back from where the female is sitting, out in the open and a few feet from a tiny pine sapling. We kid ourselves that we can make her out with the naked eye, surrounded by the fresh green fronds of emerging bracken and the pale, contorted shapes of broken pine branches. Once we raise our binoculars the bracken and branches help to guide us in to the female.

The female's camouflage mimics the colours of the ground on which she is sitting, two eggs beneath her body within a shallow scrape. Moving from binoculars to tripod and telescope we settle down to study her. While I sketch the bird and the landscape in note form, drawing together the words that will later form the basis of a poem, the two artists sketch her outline in more structural terms and, in Esther's case, mix colours that will later capture the bracken, flints and broken pine.

Being this close to the Nightjar, seemingly so confident in its camouflage, is a privilege and we all appreciate the opportunity to spend time with her and to take in not just the subtleties of her form and plumage but also to enjoy being in the forest at dusk. We are sufficiently far into the forest to have lost the sound of passing traffic – a difficult thing to achieve, even here – but the occasional crack of a rifle on the nearby range reminds us that we are not entirely clear of human activity. The bird barely moves over the course of the next two hours, with only the slightest shift in her eyelid revealing that she is alive and alert.

As dusk approaches, the research team returns to erect two mist nets, hinged at a central pole and set at right angles, the pole just a few metres from the sitting bird. The female will leave the nest to feed, perhaps called off by her mate and it is at this point that, with luck, she will be captured and tagged. It is a skilful operation, the bird caught as she comes off the

Carry Akroyd
Cuckoo
Serigraph

nest, and we take her back to the nearby car to be processed. Ian and Greg have tagged many Nightjars over several seasons and once she has been ringed, aged, sexed and measured, they will attach the tiny GPS-tag, with its short aerial, to the base of the central tail feathers. The tag will record her location on a predetermined schedule over the next few nights, charting the foraging movements that she makes and revealing her use of the forest compartments and, perhaps, the wider landscape. Harriet and Esther continue their sketching, this time capturing not just the bird but the researchers attaching the tag.

The results of the tagging have revealed that the Nightjars using Thetford Forest make regular foraging flights to sites well outside of the forest. It is likely that these sites provide good feeding opportunities, perhaps indicating that the forest alone cannot support all of their needs. Understanding the role of these sites, and how the birds use the different age compartments within the forest itself, should help to inform decisions on how the forest should be managed for the benefit of these birds. Importantly, the work may help us to understand why the Nightjar population in Thetford Forest is present at a much lower density than that located at Dersingham Bog, another site used by the species in north-west Norfolk and one where similar tagging work is being undertaken.

A few more Nightjars are fitted with tags later in the season. This time, however, the schedule for recording their location will be set with a much increased interval, allowing the tags to be left on the birds as they migrate south to their wintering grounds. The precision of these tags should allow us to gain a new insight into the migration routes, stopover sites and wintering areas used by the Nightjars breeding in Thetford Forest. As we saw earlier in the book, the first of this information is already starting to come in. As more birds are tagged, so our understanding will increase further and we can be more confident about the patterns of movement that we are seeing.

Reed Warblers

To experience a reedbed in the way that perhaps a Reed Warbler or Cuckoo does, requires you to slip on a wetsuit or a pair of chest waders and immerse yourself in a strangely vertical world. Not all reedbeds are the same, of course, and those worked by Professor Nick Davies at Wicken Fen are a little different from those that fringe the deep flooded gravel pits where Dave Leech, the BTO's Head of Ringing and Nest Recording runs his own personal study of a Reed Warbler population. Both Cuckoos and their Reed Warbler hosts were species that we wished to share with those involved in the Flight Lines project, so one summer morning we found ourselves struggling into wetsuits and chest waders at Dave's site in the Norfolk Brecks. I've helped out here over the years, but for Esther Tyson,

Harriet Mead and storyteller Malcolm Green this was a new experience. It also made an interesting contrast for Harriet and Esther, after the late nights working with Nightjars.

Thanks to his tremendous dedication and an understanding family, Dave's Reed Warbler population is well monitored; virtually every Reed Warbler nesting attempt made on the site will be monitored over the course of a surprisingly long season. A small number of the nests are parasitised by Cuckoos, usually by a single female but on occasion two may target the site. Dave knew which nests we could visit safely, to show the team both Reed Warbler and Cuckoo chicks in the nest.

Being quite low to the water's surface gives you a different perspective of a reed bed and you are first made aware of the Reed Warblers by their chattering alarm calls. Following the trail made by earlier monitoring visits we soon reach a piece of coloured electrical tape, attached to a reed stem on the edge of the trail. Dave carefully parts the reeds behind this to reveal a small woven cup, attached to a mix of live and dead reed stems and holding a clutch of Reed Warbler eggs.

A little further on and we come to another Reed Warbler nest, this time containing four small and darkly coloured chicks, naked and with their eyes yet to open. Neither of these nests has been visited by a Cuckoo. Dave knows his way around this series of old gravel pits, exploiting the gravel ridges that have been left in some of the pits and avoiding areas where deep water or deep silt could cause us difficulties. It is then that we come to another short piece of fringing reedbed, to a nest that contains a young Cuckoo, alert and sporting what can only be described as a punk hair-do, its crown feathers just emerging from pin and yet to take on the sculptured contour of an older bird.

Now that the artists and our storyteller Malcolm Green have had an overview of the site, its residents and the project work being done, we drop them off at different locations, leaving them to settle into the scene, collect their thoughts and begin the process of capturing everything in a creative way. For Malcolm in particular, this settling in and becoming part of the Reed Warbler or Cuckoo's landscape is an essential part of the creative process. It has been interesting to look at the dynamic of artists, storyteller and researchers. All show the excitement of being here, displaying a clear sense of wonder at these intimate encounters. Science may require a professional and dispassionate approach but it is easy to see why Dave, like so many other volunteers and paid professionals, loves his work and is prepared to put so much time and energy into a project like this. Just being here, in these reedbeds, is a privilege. Couple that with the knowledge that the research will take forward our understanding of these summer visitors and it becomes clear why people like Dave get involved with birds.

Photographs
Tagging Nightjars to explore movements

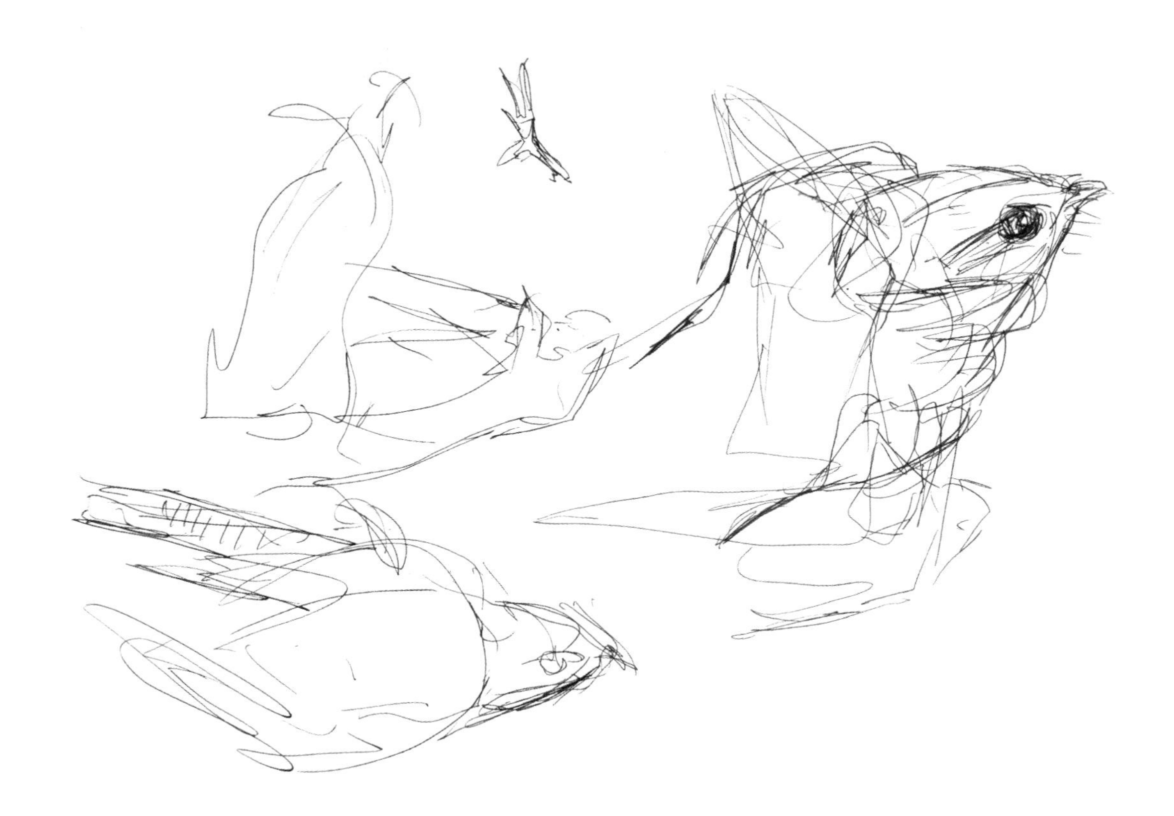

Harriet Mead
Nightjar sketches
Pen on paper

A busy season

The Reed Warbler study season runs through into late summer, keeping Dave busy for several months. For other fieldworkers, working on different species, the season can be much shorter. For those working on Willow Warblers, for example, the season is likely to begin in late April and be finished well before early August. Willow Warblers are single-brooded, putting all of their efforts into a single breeding attempt and only rarely attempting a genuine second brood.

Many of those studying the ecology of our summer migrants work on more than one species, and some volunteers participate in multiple BTO projects. Many bird ringers, for example, operate Constant Effort Sites (CES) in addition to their general ringing and single-species projects, using fine mesh nets erected in set locations once every 10 days throughout the spring and summer. Each CES ringing session usually involves a small team of ringers, arriving before dawn to erect the nets and then catching, ringing and processing the birds caught over the following hours. With some 130 or so sites being operated each year, the scheme provides valuable information on the abundance of adults and juveniles, their productivity and (in the case of adults) their survival rates. The scheme monitors a couple of dozen species of songbird, several of which are summer visitors, wintering in Africa or around the Mediterranean. The most commonly caught species in CES is Reed Warbler, closely followed by Chiffchaff and Blackcap, underlining its important contribution to our understanding of migrant birds using wet scrub and reedbed sites covered by the volunteers.

The ratio of adult to juvenile captures made on CES sites provides a simple measure of productivity, reflecting the broader productivity of the bird populations on and around CES sites. In this way, it dovetails rather neatly with the information collected by BTO nest recorders, whose efforts tell us about productivity on a per nest basis – rather than a per breeding pair basis. Changes in Blackcap productivity may, for example, stem from either changes that happen within individual nesting attempts – such as an increase in clutch size over time – or from a change in the number of breeding attempts made. Nest Record data can tell us about the former but not the latter, while CES gives us a measure that combines the two.

An important component of these national monitoring schemes is that they collect information from across a broad range of sites, both in terms of their geography and the habitats they contain. As we saw earlier in the book for UK Cuckoos, regional differences in migration patterns have been linked to different population trajectories, so it is important not to draw conclusions about what is happening to a particular species from observations that are derived from a single site or small number of sites. More is very much better when it comes to monitoring. Of course, broad scale national monitoring

Esther Tyson
Nightjar
Oil

cannot always provide the depth or detail that might be needed, particularly where what is being asked of volunteers has to be simplified to account for regional differences, ease of participation or commitment of time. Those who tend to focus on a particular species through a personal project often commit more time and energy to their work, though at the expense of not being able to contribute to other projects and studies. This is where networks of volunteers, perhaps operating as part of a ringing group, can make a big difference, drawing in additional people when needed and sharing the load.

Working more widely

We've spent much of this chapter looking at the volunteers and how they contribute to our understanding of migrant ecology and changing migrant populations. These volunteers are as much part of this story as the birds themselves, and it was important for the artists participating in the Flight Lines project to work with and document their activities. In addition to those examples already mentioned, other SWLA artists spent time with volunteers at sites across the UK. Monitoring of the Sand Martin colony in the artificial nesting bank at Attenborough Nature Reserve in Nottinghamshire, for example, was captured through the visits that Esther Tyson made to the site, these providing a neat comparison to the Sand Martin colony in a natural bank captured in the series of paintings produced by Michael Warren.

The Sand Martin work at Attenborough underlines the link between the work of volunteers monitoring the changing fortunes of migrant birds and the conservation action being directed towards them. The bank at Attenborough was completed in 2014 and built with the help of the Heritage Lottery Fund. Some 150 nest holes are spread over three different faces, incorporated into the design to account for the strong prevailing winds at the site. Integral to the bank is access for nest recorders and ringers, ensuring that the contribution of the bank can be documented through regular monitoring. Importantly, the bank also has a special bird hide built into its side, allowing members of the public visiting the site to secure close-up views of the Sand Martins as they visit their nests.

Another recent project with a clear link to conservation action is the partnership between BTO and Anglian Water, centred around Nightingales. The work, which has also involved Anglian Water staff and volunteers, seeks to understand why Nightingales have declined by a staggering 90% in the UK since the 1960s and to share habitat management practices that have been developed off the back of research work and practical conservation efforts. The Nightingale has tremendous cultural resonance; for this reason it can be considered one of our most important summer migrants, a species that can act as a champion for others that have a much lower profile.

Video stills
Reed Warbler feeding
its chicks in the nest

The decline in Nightingale populations has been linked to a number of different factors, some operating here on the breeding grounds and others operating elsewhere. BTO and other research provides strong evidence that deer browsing within woodland and scrub sites is having a negative impact on Nightingale numbers. Nightingale breeding territories typically contain thickets of dense vegetation, beneath which is bare ground over which the birds can forage for food. Growing deer populations have led to an increase in browsing pressure and a reduction in the sorts of habitat features upon which the Nightingales depend. Without this low cover, sites can no longer support Nightingales and we have seen their loss from many former breeding sites.

Conditions on the wintering grounds, most notably changes in land use and habitat, are also likely to have carry-over effects into the breeding season. Understanding where our Nightingales winter, and in which habitats, is an important first step to determining how changing conditions in Africa could be mediated to reduce their impact on our wintering birds. The tagging work being carried out by BTO, much of it in partnership with Anglian Water, is already starting to generate important information in this regard, but more detailed work within West Africa will also be needed.

Closer to home, several studies have highlighted the benefit of habitat management for this species, involving coppicing and control of deer numbers to promote the heterogeneous vegetation structure that the birds need. Traditionally, the Nightingale was regarded as a woodland bird, strongly associated with coppice. However, over recent decades it has become apparent that scrub habitats have become increasingly important for the species. By focusing new research effort towards this habitat it has been possible to produce management advice that can be used to create the right vegetation structure for Nightingales. Scrub is a dynamic habitat, suitable for Nightingales for only a decade at best in most circumstances. The development of appropriate cutting regimes means that those managing sites with scrub and Nightingales should now be able to retain their birds by cutting on a rotation to ensure a continual supply of suitable habitat.

Doing the research

It is only through understanding the ecology and behaviour of our summer migrants that we can begin to tackle the underlying causes driving their population declines. While some of this work has very clear links to the conservation action that may follow, much of it can seem a bit removed, perhaps being less readily applied. However, it is this basic knowledge about migrants and their migrations that forms the building blocks onto which later more applied work can be built. In the case of the Nightingale example that we have just examined, knowing that Nightingales struggle to recolonise sites from where they have disappeared informs where habitat management efforts should be targeted – they should be directed at sites close to others where the species still occurs, rather than to sites that are located many miles away. Bird ringing and detailed field studies suggest either that natal dispersal (how far a young bird moves from where it was born to where it will first breed) or breeding dispersal (how far an adult bird will move between successive breeding attempts) are low, or that individual Nightingales are more likely to settle near to others of their kind rather than settle at new sites.

The efforts of CES volunteers, or those participating in the BTO's Retrapping Adults for Survival scheme, help to unpick the differences that exist between species, populations or age/sex classes, which might lead to birds wintering in different areas or using different migration routes. We need to understand all of this information before we can be confident about how successful a planned conservation action might be. The tracking studies of which we have heard much throughout this book, can also help us to identify important stopover sites for particular species or populations, delivering the evidence that will be needed to support applications for the designation of protected status. Understanding how all of this information can be brought together for the benefit of migrant birds, and exploring what else we might need to do, is the focus of our final chapter.

Harriet Mead
'Funnel'
Welded found objects

protection

Personal Narrative

The hottest day of the year and I'm walking around a reserve in the middle of the Brecks, Norfolk, in my wetsuit? Why? Good question. For a start I'm expecting to jump in the water at any moment… but first, the tour! A lovely little reserve of reclaimed gravel pits. Warblers, Reed Bunting, Grass Snake! There's a female Cuckoo in the distance and we are expecting to see young Cuckoo in the nest!

Oh my goodness, wading through the reeds waist high in chilling water and we see one of the finest Reed Warbler nests, almost missed it. Inside is the tiniest little pink creature. A one day old Cuckoo chick with two remaining warbler eggs! Quite a find! Harriet Mead and I return the following day and the chick is already changing colour AND he's on his own! We leave him be and skirt back around the edge of the reedbed. Finding the short marker, I veer to the right and head between tall reeds, along a water filled alley and there to our right is nest DIL070.

Wow, we are looking at a 12 day old Cuckoo chick. A beautiful creature amply filling its adopted home! Black and white from a distance and then he opens his mouth! What a gape! Amazingly MASSIVE orange expectant gape. It's easy to fall in love with these parasitic birds.

Esther Tyson
SWLA artist

The future

I can recall the day as clearly as if it were yesterday. It was April and we were in the Surrey/Hampshire borderlands leading a training course for BTO nest recorders. The weather was unseasonably poor and we were descending into the Devil's Punch Bowl, a deep valley alongside the A3 at Hindhead, where we would spend time watching Tree Pipits, Woodlarks and Redstarts back to their nests. This is a site that I know from my youth, a site where Redstarts and Wood Warblers used to be common and where I used to birdwatch or search for reptiles and insects. As we work our way down the steep slope, our gaze firmly fixed on the wet and treacherous path, we catch a few phrases of song that clutch at the memory. The singer is a little distant but still unmistakable; it is a Wood Warbler, a species I thought had been lost from the county some years back. The previous Wood Warbler nest seen locally had been during the year we had first run a nest recording course here; the nest had been predated and was, quite possibly, the last nesting attempt of a bird that had since disappeared from the area.

Working our way across the slope we are drawn towards the singer, finally emerging above a small patch of more mature woodland. We soon spot the bird, his song rich and sibilant just as the text books describe. The quantity of song that this male delivers over the coming minutes suggests that he is alone and unmated. Were he to have a mate nearby he would not sing so strongly. The knowledge that this bird, which has travelled the vast distance back from Africa, is unpaired adds a sense of poignancy to the moment. Here is a species, once so strongly associated with the Beech woods of my youth, that has slipped from our grasp over the course of just a few decades. Of course, it isn't just from here that the Wood Warbler has been lost; the run of national bird atlases reveal a pattern of decline across much of its former range. This song, such a central component of my childhood soundscape, will no longer be part of the soundscape for the new generations of Surrey birdwatchers who now walk these Beech hangers.

A cultural heritage

Our cultural attachment to migrant birds is significant and it is perhaps unsurprising that these birds, which mark the changing of the seasons, should feature so prominently in our literature, music and art. Many of the pieces written, composed or painted, depicting Swallows, Swifts, Nightingales and others, come from personal connection. You can, for example, sense the relief and exhilaration of the poet Ted Hughes, when he proclaims '*They've made it again, which means the globe's still working*' in his poem Swifts. Over the years I spent living in a small market town, I too felt the joy of the Swift's return and the emptiness when the screaming parties vacated the air over the town to begin their journey south.

We notice our summer migrants and winter visitors because they are only here for part of the year. At the same time we fail to notice the hidden migrants, like Blackbird, Song Thrush and Chaffinch, birds for which the UK is both a destination and a year-round home. Yet if Scandinavian Chaffinches stopped visiting us for the winter we would notice the drop in numbers at our garden feeding stations, but maybe not comprehend the reasons behind the change observed.

This engagement with our summer migrants, even evident within those who profess just a casual passing interest in birds and wildlife, gives me hope that we can secure the support that we need to understand why many are in decline. We cannot act alone, however, since migrants, by definition, roam freely over political borders. That cultural awareness of migrants is certainly shared more widely across Europe, and this is one of the reasons why so much of the research into migrant birds has been collaborative, involving researchers from many different countries. Collaboration delivers a stronger collective voice, of the kind needed to sway the interests of governments and corporations at a scale that matters for birds who can range hundreds or even many thousands of miles over the course of a year.

As you increase the scale, from country to region to continent and beyond, so it becomes more difficult to secure collaboration and deliver a consistent approach to migrant conservation. Cultural differences, such as those evident within Europe in relation to the hunting of migrant birds, can undermine attempts to deliver on legislation that has wider political backing. Hunting, for example, has a strong cultural importance for much of Maltese society and this has created an inertia within the Maltese government, meaning that it is reluctant to enforce or enact legislation to which it has signed up at a wider European level. In many ways this underlines the importance of taking the conservation messages around migrant birds to the communities who live alongside them, rather than solely to those who may be in power, but removed from the countryside and its wildlife.

The challenge of africa

The fact that migrant birds move between countries quite clearly presents something of a challenge for those wishing to secure their conservation. Not only is it necessary to build up a detailed understanding of the species concerned in each of the countries through which they pass, it is also necessary to secure a consistent commitment to their conservation from across the broad range of stakeholders. We know a great deal about the ecology of our summer migrants from here in Britain and western Europe but we know rather less about where they winter, the types of site that they use, the change in resources available to them and very many other things. Addressing this lack of knowledge is the first step to securing the evidence needed to garner the necessary support at both government and international level.

That it is possible to secure international support can be seen from treaties and conventions, such as the UN's Convention on Migratory Species, to which many countries have become signatories. Such documents recognise the problems facing migratory species and emphasise our obligations to tackle them, but governments face many different problems and have many different obligations, some of which conflict with one another. Africa, for example, is home to some of the poorest people in the world; a wish to reduce poverty and deliver economic growth and social well-being for her citizens has driven much of the change in land use that has been identified as being detrimental to biodiversity, including to those bird species that migrate between Africa, Europe and Asia each year.

Agricultural development is seen as a mechanism for reducing poverty and delivering economic growth across large parts of Africa, something which is supported by current figures from the World Bank which suggest that agriculture supports or directly employs two thirds of Africa's labour force. If policy decisions about the nature of this agricultural development can draw on scientific evidence, be informed by local communities and be underpinned and shaped by environmental and social standards and laws, then there is hope for a sustainable future. Managing the environment for birds and other wildlife can be good for people too and there is increasing recognition of the ecosystem services – such as delivering clean air and clean water – that stem from managing the environment in a sustainable manner, realising long term benefits for people and wildlife.

It is important to realise, however, that there are also outside influences, such as the multinational companies, who own increasing amounts of African land and agricultural commodities. Such companies present both opportunities and difficulties, adding to the political and economic complexities that need to be addressed when considering the conservation of Afro-Palearctic migrants.

Carry Akroyd
Secured Ground
Serigraph

Personal Narrative

I'd never seen a Stone-curlew before and still wouldn't have seen one even now except for the expert 'stoney-spotters' getting my eye in. Surreptitious and stealthy, the leggy birds sneak around their nest area, so camouflaged in their colours against the background that they can only be spotted when they move.

Which is why they need the right Stone-curlew–coloured background. A mix of browns and grey and white and black; some rough sandy earth in light and dark browns, rough enough for some dips and shadows, some pale and dark stones, short dry grasses and shrivelled sparse herbs. Given the right décor, the stonies can move in.

I am always interested in context, the landscape as it appears to the bird's territorial and dinner-focused perceptions. I had driven across Breckland many times. I was familiar with the windbreak pine lines leaning along the straight field edges, but I had never actually stopped and walked on the ground. The sandy soil is almost an inland beach, and the irrigation systems ubiquitous.

One of the ideal habitats we looked at was doubly protected, as it was within an army base. Between the pill-boxes and bullet-cases, the thin uncultivated ground supported not only the rare birds but also flowering herbs, flowers once so common in the wild but now needing the army to defend them. Rabbits disturb the ground just enough to help the birds make a small scrape in which to lay completely camouflaged eggs. So my introduction to a new species was also my introduction to a new kind of habitat, the two completely paired.

Carry Akroyd
SWLA artist

It is also important to recognise that much of the conservation sector sits outside of Africa, and we must be careful to act in ways that are appropriate, sensitive and supportive. Recognising that the migrant birds that breed here in Britain are not ours but, as we have seen through the journeys described in this book, spend their time in different places and with other people and cultures, seems like a good place to start. Birds are global travellers and it is time that we took more notice of that. Understanding the extent to which the people who encounter 'our' migrants elsewhere recognise them, or understand that these visiting birds spend part of the year elsewhere, is an essential step. If we can understand how they interact with and view these birds, then there is the opportunity to begin a dialogue about them, to build a common understanding and, I hope, deliver an approach to their conservation. What that conservation action looks like in practical terms very much depends on identifying what it is that is driving their population change. It is only once we can establish what needs to be done that we can begin to discuss how to do it.

Providing the evidence

Throughout this book we have seen examples where researchers and volunteers, often working in partnership, have been collecting information that tells us about migrant birds: about where they winter, the routes they use and how these vary between species, populations and individuals. In the UK we are fortunate to have a long history of monitoring bird populations, generating information that reveals how their populations are faring. In many cases this knowledge has prompted targeted work to identify the factors driving the observed changes – something that BTO researchers have been very good at doing.

By looking across species it has been possible to highlight groups of species, such as Afro-Palearctic migrants, where a common cause, or causes, is likely to be driving change. Having identified that there is a problem, then – as has been the case with summer migrants – the BTO has been able to direct fundraising efforts and the resulting resources towards it. The programme of migrant work, from research into links between wintering area and changes in climate and land use, through to the tagging studies seeking to identify migration routes and stopover sites, has already delivered a great deal of new information, forming the evidence that will be needed to direct conservation action. But there is more to do, and for some species we are only just beginning to answer the most basic questions. We still do not know, for example, where our House Martins winter or where our Tree Pipits and Whinchats stopover on migration.

We have seen examples throughout the book of instances where rainfall conditions in West Africa have been linked to declines within UK breeding populations. BTO data have been key to much of this work, often carried out at the level of individual species. More recently, we have been able to look across species to see if the relationship applies more generally across the broader suite of species wintering in the region. Nancy Ockendon is one of those to have led on this work for BTO, her analyses revealing that Sahelian rainfall has strong and consistent effects on migrant populations, positively influencing the population growth rate for six of nine species which winter in this area. There is also increasing evidence that migrants wintering further south are in trouble and again we can look for linkages between conditions in Africa and population trends here in the UK, teasing out what is driving the declines seen and where it is exerting its influence.

Other work, this time carried out with academic collaborators at the University of East Anglia and the University of Sheffield, has sought to understand the extent to which effects from the non-breeding ranges can 'carry over' and influence breeding performance. This work has focused on three species of conservation concern – Redstart, Spotted Flycatcher and Wood Warbler – revealing that, for example, warm conditions during spring passage through the Mediterranean promote earlier breeding in all three species. Interestingly, the carry over effects also influence breeding performance to a greater extent than weather conditions experienced on the breeding grounds. High levels of rainfall in the Sahel lead to an increase in Redstart brood size and better spring passage conditions are associated with an increase in Spotted Flycatcher brood size and the number of Wood Warbler chicks fledging (though the latter effect is less pronounced).

These findings underline that the impacts of factors operating elsewhere on things that happen here in the UK need to be considered when assessing why migrant populations have changed. Such evidence reinforces the need for conservation efforts to be coordinated across the full geographical range of these migrant species. Fixing things here in the UK for breeding Nightingales, by reducing the impacts of scrub removal and deer browsing, may not be sufficient to halt the observed decline if what is happening within Africa is just as important.

Sharing expertise

The evidence that we are gathering on migrant birds from here within the UK, together with that collected remotely from Africa about, for example, rainfall patterns and land use change, may in itself not be enough to pinpoint the causes of migrant decline. There is a need for field studies to examine how migrants use their wintering areas and the habitats they contain, their diet and behaviour. We have already seen the importance of this more detailed approach from, for example, the UK work on Nightjars discussed in the previous chapter, but that is only part of the story.

If we are to replicate this approach within Africa then we cannot simply presume to send UK researchers to Africa to collect the information required. In some cases political circumstances prevent access to those areas where some of our migrant species spend the winter. This is one of the reasons why we were able to send a Flight Lines team to sites in Gabon used by UK Cuckoos but not to sites further east in the Democratic Republic of Congo, where many of our other Cuckoos spend the winter.

Working in partnership with in-country organisations is an important component for any project that seeks to collect new information from the wintering grounds. Although such organisations are often far smaller than their European equivalents, less well resourced and without access to large and established networks of volunteer fieldworkers, they are staffed by individuals with tremendous knowledge and enthusiasm. Investing in these local relationships, as BirdLife International has been able to do so effectively, should be viewed as an essential step towards securing the evidence needed to support conservation action across the flyway.

Capacity building is another area where European organisations can help to secure more resources and expertise within Africa. Some of this can be achieved through programmes like the University of Cambridge's MPhil in Conservation Leadership. The MPhil course is based in the University's Department of Geography, which is collaborating with partners in the Cambridge Conservation Initiative (CCI) to deliver the course. CCI brings together eight internationally renowned conservation organisations, including the BTO, together with the University of Cambridge and a network of others belonging to the Cambridge Conservation Forum. CCI partners occupy offices in the refurbished David Attenborough Building in central Cambridge, embedding the Masters in Conservation Leadership students with world leading conservation practitioners and researchers.

BTO has also been working to build capacity within West Africa through other avenues. Thanks to the very generous support of the A G Leventis Foundation, BTO staff have been working directly with universities, masters students and local BirdLife partners in Africa. It is this wish to increase the potential to conserve birds in Africa, through partnership working and the sharing of expertise, that stands the best chance of securing engagement from different communities as we collectively seek to mitigate impacts of land use change on wildlife. This work is also acting as a springboard for research into the movements of migrant birds within Africa and efforts to understand their strategies for taking advantage of seasonal food resources.

Important areas within Africa

If we are to secure a future for migrant birds, wintering in Africa, then one option would be to establish a series of protected sites covering those

Darren Woodhead
Goldcrest and Swallows
Watercolour

areas identified as being important for migrants. Another, and perhaps better, option would be to secure land use and management strategies more widely across the continent that are more compatible with the long term survival of migrant populations. These two different approaches reflect the land-sparing versus land-sharing argument that has become a feature of many conservation discussions. Do we manage most of the land intensively for our needs, sparing small areas that are set aside for wildlife, or do we manage the land as a whole much less intensively so that wildlife can continue to live alongside us? These two approaches have been explored by BTO researchers, working with colleagues at Makere University in Uganda, NatureUganda and others. The work, which was published in 2013, examined an area in southern Uganda which was associated with the cultivation of coffee and bananas. Surveys across both farmland and forest habitats along a gradient of agricultural intensification enabled the team to relate population densities of 256 bird species (including 10 Afro-Palearctic migrants) to crop yields, farm income and the degree of agricultural intensification. The results, which were consistent with similar work carried out in India and Ghana, revealed that most bird species did better under land-sparing approaches. In these areas more native forest was left unaffected by agriculture. Whilst this work does suggest that high-yield farming can be effective in delivering land-sparing, it can only work if it is combined with robust measures to protect natural habitats, other ecosystem services and human livelihoods.

Where should we protect migrant birds?

One of the challenges we face before we can talk about protected areas is how to identify where these should be placed. Various criteria have been developed for this purpose which, for example, may favour those sites that contain a large number of individual birds or a significant part of one or more species' populations. BirdLife International already includes this criterion in those used to distinguish Important Bird Areas (IBAs). Another approach is to select sites that are hotspots for species richness, that richness perhaps categorised by the rarity of the species concerned. Again, this approach has been incorporated into the selection criteria for IBAs, with BirdLife International recognising sets of sites that '*together hold a suite of restricted-range species or biome-restricted species*'. A rather different approach, which is based on the principle of complementarity, would be to seek to preserve a full complement of species in the maximum number of sites possible but at the least cost.

Using a database holding information on the distribution of migrant birds within Africa, it has been possible for researchers to identify key regions within the continent. This work has, depending upon the criterion used, identified a number of different areas, some of which are important under multiple criteria. Some of the most recent work has underlined the special importance of the Sahel, especially the most western and eastern parts of the region. Given the rapid pace of change within the Sahel, with the continued expansion of intensive agriculture and loss of natural and semi-natural habitats, there is an urgent need to identify and achieve some key conservation objectives here. Other important areas include: Central Sudan, northern Ethiopia and the Red Sea coast along Eritrea, Djibouti and north-west Somalia; Uganda, Tanzania and Kenya; and northern Zimbabwe.

A key contribution to identifying important areas will come from the growing amounts of information on stopover sites, since these are likely to be just as important as those sites used for breeding or wintering. If the success or failure of a migration hinges on the resources available at a stopover site used prior to the crossing of a major ecological barrier, such as the Sahara desert, then failure to recognise its importance could be catastrophic for the species concerned. This makes efforts to secure this knowledge for our Afro-Palearctic migrants all the more important. Improvements in the technology used to track migrant birds, and in particular the continuing miniaturisation of devices, means that we are increasingly able to tag and follow species that just a year or two ago would not have been possible.

It is also worth just noting that birds are effective indicators of wider biodiversity, suggesting that areas good for birds are also likely to be good for other species. Unsurprisingly therefore, many of the IBAs identified are also recognised as Key Biodiversity Areas (KBAs) for other plants and animals. KBAs are defined as sites that '*contribute to the global persistence of biodiversity, including vital habitat for threatened plant and animal species in terrestrial, freshwater and marine ecosystems*' and, as for IBAs, their selection is based on strict criteria. Increasing recognition of KBAs as a conservation tool is likely to benefit birds, including those that winter in Africa but breed in the UK.

Seeking connection

Tagging birds is not cheap; a satellite tag typically costs several thousand pounds, with an ongoing and annual cost to access the data as it comes on stream. Individual governments are unlikely to fund this type of research, so organisations like the BTO (and others) have to raise the money from the members, supporters and other individuals who care about what happens to these birds.

Making people aware of the work being done and explaining the urgency associated with the need to reverse migrant declines before species like Turtle Dove, Cuckoo and Nightingale are lost from the UK,

is really important. This is one of the reasons why the BTO understood that it needed to put resources into the BTO/SWLA Flight Lines project. Much of the work being done by BTO staff and volunteers is published in peer-reviewed journals, highly academic in nature and rather dry to a casual reader. Although the work is then usually reported through scheme newsletters, the BTO's membership magazine, social media or other communications channels, it can lack the personal connection that readers need if they are to truly engage with what is being said.

Art is a medium through which personal connection can be achieved, often working far more effectively than the written word. Enabling SWLA member artists to engage with the fieldwork and science being carried out by the BTO provides an opportunity for a different way of looking at migrant birds to capture what is happening to them. This can then be shared with new audiences, introducing them to migrants and the conservation issues that they face. In addition, and importantly, the partnering of artist and scientist also encourages the scientist to look at their research work in a different way. No longer is it dry and rigorously academic, becoming instead something that has life and energy, an urgency and an impact. It has been amazing to experience the transformations in some of those researchers who have been part of this amazing project. Chris Hewson, in particular, has developed his understanding of how BTO work on Cuckoos, Swifts and Nightingales can be presented to a far broader audience than is typically reached by scientists. This is perhaps best exemplified by his sharing a stage with the photojournalist Toby Smith and storyteller Malcolm Green at a sell-out event showcasing the Cuckoo, its role in culture and the work that is being done to save it.

Looking to the future

There are several major problems that make declining migrant populations a significant conservation challenge. One of these is the gaps that remain in our understanding of where migrant birds actually winter. For many declining migrants we are only just beginning to discover these sites and, even for those where we have some knowledge, this is usually restricted to a handful of breeding populations – sometimes even just a handful of individuals – rather than for the breeding range as a whole. New initiatives, such as the work taking place to understand the movements of Chinese Cuckoos, which has been supported by BTO expertise, are further demonstrating the importance of Africa on a wider global scale. At least some Chinese Cuckoos, it seems, also winter in Africa but more tagging work is needed before we can build up a more complete picture of their movements.

As we have just seen, a second problem is that of scale. While there are some relatively small areas of great importance to migrant birds, it is

Robert Greenhalf
Wagtails and Squacco
Monoprint

becoming increasingly clear that much larger parts of the African continent are key, as evident from the movements made within Africa by wintering Swifts and Nightjars. Unless there is systematic change in land management practices across large parts of the African continent then we will be unable to halt the decline in migrant bird populations. It is also worth noting that land use change is a potential issue for a much wider range of species. A recent review of the resident bird, native plant and mammal populations within the Sahel reached a similar conclusion, arguing that there needs to be a 30–100% increase in Africa's reserve system in order to reach even the most basic conservation targets.

We should, however, be hopeful for the future. With increasing levels of collaboration, new innovations in technology, and a willingness to secure a future for our migrant birds, we have the opportunity to do something. We must not be blinkered in our actions, by pretending that other needs (such as tackling poverty in West Africa) can be ignored, and we must work towards solutions that are inclusive and recognise the sometimes competing calls on resources and land. Most of all we must not lose sight of the birds themselves, and the other communities with whom they share part of the year. While we may consider that things need to be done in Africa to secure the future of 'our' summer migrants, we also need to recognise that we need to do things here, within Europe, in order to safeguard the future of Africa's winter visitors. These are not 'our' birds alone, they are shared by many others and we all have a duty to conserve them for each other and for the birds themselves.

The BTO/SWLA Flight Lines project has given us an opportunity to tell the stories of some of the birds that migrate to and from Africa, following their journeys from when they leave our shores in autumn through to their return, and to share the tremendous generosity, industry and passion of those who work to study and understand them. Without this generosity our knowledge of migrant birds – and indeed of resident birds – would be very much poorer, and the chances of us securing a future for them would be very much reduced. Thank you to everyone who has given their time and energy to migrant birds, to the work of the BTO and its partners and to the BTO/SWLA Flight Lines project.

Dafila Scott
Swifts, courtship flight
Pastel

Personal Narrative

It is a still evening, the air warm and there is a sense that the thickening clouds might break to release a cooling shower. The ground within this block of clearfell is rough and uneven, scattered with the bleached bones of broken pines and the bright green fronds of bracken. We are here to catch a Nightjar, part of a tagging project being operated by BTO researchers Ian Henderson and Greg Conway. Joining us tonight are SWLA artists Esther Tyson and Harriet Mead, here to document the bird, its habitat and those studying its behaviour and ecology.

Lines of newly planted pines grid the clearfell. A few rows back from where we are standing are several stout branches, placed into the ground like some form of totem. These are our marker and guide us onto the female Nightjar incubating her two eggs just a few feet to the left. The bird is beautifully camouflaged, an extension of the broken ground in feathered form. Sat facing right, her eye open ever-so slightly, she is aware of our presence but confident in her camouflage.

Over the next two hours we sit and watch, Esther and Harriet sketching the bird and capturing the colours that make up this forest palette. I take notes, preparing material that will ultimately shape itself into the woven lines of a poem. It is a wonderfully immersive experience to be here, to see this bird on her breeding site and to share in the sights, sounds and smells of the forest at dusk... to hear '*the buzz of a late fly and the crack of a rifle on the range*.'

Mike Toms
BTO volunteer nest recorder and ringer

Notes

Swallows gathering on wires is a sign of summer's end and the approach of autumn migration. Swallows/© Fabrice Cahez – naturepl.com pp.2–3.

The project took artists, researchers and volunteers to many different places, as these images show. Clockwise from top left; Sahel landscape, Phil Atkinson; Po Watershed, Chris Hewson; Po Watershed, Chris Hewson; Welsh woodland, Mike Toms; Senegal fishermen, Robert Greenhalf; Baobabs, Phil Atkinson, Portland lighthouse, Rob Read/Nature Photographers; Clearfell, Mike Toms. p.8.

The woodlands of western Britain are home to important populations of Pied Flycatcher, Redstart and Wood Warbler. Photo/Mike Toms. pp.10–11.

Much of our understanding of migrant birds comes from the work of volunteers, adding to their enjoyment of birds by participating in BTO surveys. BirdTrack volunteers/David Tipling. pp.12–13.

Migrant birds are not 'ours'; instead they share parts of their year with other communities across the globe. African children/Esther Tyson. pp.14–15.

Between 1967 and 2014, UK Turtle Dove populations declined by 97%, making this attractive dove one of our most threatened summer migrants and prompting research to understand its decline. Turtle Dove/Edmund Fellowes. p.16

As part of the Flight Lines project we sent three SWLA artists to the bird observatory on Bardsey, a small island off the Welsh coast. Kim Atkinson, Greg Poole and Darren Woodhead joined Steve Stancliffe and his wife Emma – also an artist – at the Observatory to watch and document the work that goes on to collect information on the birds breeding on the island – including a colony of Manx Shearwaters – and passing through. Photographs of the artists and volunteers at work/ Kim Atkinson, Greg Poole and Darren Woodhead. p.41.

Vast numbers of migrating birds pass through Israel on their journey south, often gathering in large numbers to take advantage of favourable weather. White Storks, Paul Sterry/Nature Photographers p.48.

In 2013, BirdLife Malta operated a Spring Watch Camp to highlight the issue of illegal hunting and trapping in Malta. Photographer David Tipling documented the project through a series of compelling images. The project also involved SWLA artist Kim Atkinson, whose work appears on the following spread. Clockwise from top left; a hunter out to shoot Turtle Doves and Quail; Maltese birdwatchers monitoring bird migration and hunting activity; local police with confiscated Turtle Doves and equipment; documenting hunting activity; injured Bee-eater euthanased because of its injuries; confiscated equipment and birds; Turtle Dove shot by hunter; a volunteer with confiscated equipment. All images © David Tipling – naturepl.com pp.62–63.

Once widespread within the UK as a breeding species, the Red-backed Shrike is now most familiar to birdwatchers as a passage migrant. Paul Sterry/ Nature Photographers. p.68.

As part of the Flight Lines project we sent four SWLA Artists (Robert Greenhalf, Bruce Pearson, Greg Poole and Esther Tyson) to Senegal in the company of Phil Atkinson, the BTO's Head of International Research. Over two weeks, the team visited sites used by migrant birds from western Europe and documented both the birds and the landscapes through a series of artworks. Sahelian landscape with Baobabs/Phil Atkinson. p.84.

The BTO/SWLA Flight Lines trip to Senegal was documented through photographs by Phil Atkinson, Robert Greenhalf, Bruce Pearson, Greg Poole and Esther Tyson. The team was supported in country by Paul Robinson and greatly aided by many other individuals. pp. 115–117.

Ringing studies suggest that migrating Wheatears do not carry large fat reserves, but instead rely on finding food at stopover sites. Being an active ground-foraging species, they can probably find sufficient insect prey at sites where other species might struggle. Wheatear/Morris Rendall. p.126.

The BTO's work tracking UK Cuckoos has taken the team to many different parts of the UK, from RAF Fylingdales in the North York Moors to the New Forest and the valleys of Wales. Much of this work has been documented by photojournalist Toby Smith, by the BTO team and other staff. Clockwise from top left; broadcasting Cuckoo calls to lure birds in, Toby Smith; Working in Yorkshire, Toby Smith; Measuring a Cuckoo's wing-length, Toby Smith, Releasing a tagged bird, Toby Smith; Using a stuffed Cuckoo to attract birds towards the net, Mike Toms; the Yorkshire Team, Toby Smith; Tagging a Cuckoo, Toby Smith; Setting the nets in Norfolk, Mike Toms. p.131.

The tracking devices used on UK Cuckoos, produced by Microwave Telemetry, have revolutionised our understanding of Cuckoo migration. A two gram satellite-tag/Mike Toms p.140-141.

Toby Smith's photography project formed the principal outputs of a Leverhulme Trust Artist's Residency at The University of Cambridge Conservation Institute. The project was joint funded in conjunction with the British Trust for Ornitholigy (BTO), Society for Wildlife Artists (SWLA), Economic and Social Research Council (ESRC) and two anonymous donors. The trip was completed, with Malcolm Green – an oral storyteller, to document the exact physical landscapes revealed by a unique study on satellite tagged Cuckoos completed by Dr Chris Hewson of the BTO. p.145-147.

The return of Sedge Warblers to UK reedbeds is charted by those birdwatchers contributing records through BirdTrack. Sedge Warbler/Graham Catley. p.150.

Being able to share the work being done to monitor, understand and ultimately conserve migrant birds is an important part of the BTO's work. With its huge audiences, BBC Springwatch has enabled us to showcase ringing and nest recording, while training courses and mentoring enable us to work with smaller groups of interested people and individual volunteers. All images by Mike Toms. p.164-165.

People are often surprised to discover that many migrant birds nest on or near the ground, but for many nest recorders, low cover – such as this dead bracken – is an ideal place to search for nesting birds, like Robin, Yellowhammer and Chiffchaff. Dave Leech nest monitoring/Mike Toms. p.166-167.

The Stone-curlew is a scare breeder, but thanks to the work of the RSPB, volunteers and the landowners on whose land these birds breed, the population has been increasing. The use of colour rings enables these birds to be monitored and identified at distance. Stone-curlew removing eggshell/Chris Knights. p.168.

As part of the Flight Lines project we took SWLA artists out with the team of BTO researchers and volunteers studying the Nightjars of Thetford Forest. Images from top left; Walking in to the site in some forest clearfell, Mike Toms; setting the nets near a nest, Jody Lawrence; two Nightjar chicks, Mike Toms; the Nightjar nest hidden within the bracken, Mike Toms; tiny tags that record where the Nightjars forage over several nights, Jody Lawrence; processing a Nightjar, Jody Lawrence, checking for moult, Jody Lawrence; SWLA artists Esther Tyson and Harriet Mead watching a sitting Nightjar, Mike Toms. p.182.

BTO staff member and volunteer Dave Leech is using high definition nest cameras to record activity at his Reed Warbler nests. This approach enables him to identify the adult birds on his study site, most of whom carry a colour ring with a unique combination of letters and numbers. On this visit the visiting bird leans in without revealing its ring. Video stills/Dave Leech. pp.188-189.

The Cuckoos parasitising the nests of Reed Warblers lay eggs that are fairly similar in size, colour and pattern to the eggs of their host, though they are not always successful in pulling off the deception. Cuckoo egg (left) and Reed Warblers eggs/Mike Toms. p.192.

The Cuckoo is a bird full of character, a species whose arrival marks the changing season and heralds the arrival of summer. Cuckoo, Edmund Fellowes. p.196.

To be out in the forest at dusk and to have the opportunity to see Nightjars at close quarters is a real privilege, and it is easy to see why volunteer ringers and nest recorders put in the hours that they do. Watching the Nightjar nets, Jody Lawrence Photographers. pp.212-213.

Thanks

The BTO/SWLA Flight Lines Project would not have been possible without the generosity of those who supported us, both financially and through giving their time. A particular thanks is owed to the generous legacy left by Penny Hollow and the kindness of her executors. Penny, a long-standing BTO member, was a regular at SWLA exhibitions, a great supporter and a lay member of the society. The bringing together of artists and scientists to raise the profile of our African migrants is a fitting tribute to her interests.

Huge thanks are also owed to the SWLA member artists who participated in the project – Carry Akroyd, Kim Atkinson, Brin Edwards, Federico Gemma, Robert Greenhalf, Richard Johnson, Szabolcs Kókay, Harriet Mead, Bruce Pearson, Nik Pollard, Greg Poole, Dafila Scott, Jane Smith, John Threlfall, Esther Tyson, Matt Underwood, Michael Warren, Darren Woodhead – and to Tim Dalling, Malcolm Green, Jody Lawrence, Toby Smith and Emma Stansfield who also brought their enthusiasm and creativity to the project.

We are particularly indepted to the volunteers, staff and other individuals who supported the artists, photographers and storyteller, gave them access to projects and embraced what we were trying to achieve: Bill Adams, Phil Atkinson, Jeff Baker, Bardsey Bird Observatory, Phil Carter, Dan Chamberlain, Andy Clements, Greg Conway, John Fanshawe, Kevin Hemsley, Ian Henderson, Chris Hewson, Angela Knapp, Dave Leech, Alicia Normand, North Solway Ringing Group, Paul Robinson, Tim Sexton, John Skilling, Steve Stansfield.

Thank you also to those who helped with the production of this book and supported the broader project. In addition to those already meantioned, we would like to say a special thank you to: Shelley Bolderson, Jo Clark, Emma Douglas, Ieuan Evans, Sam Rider, Kate Risely, Viola Ross-Smith, Sandra Sparkes and Juliet Vickery.

Index